'You can't me...

'What can't I mean...

'You want me to st... ...ntract is the price of my agreemen...

'I want you to spend some time with me,' Mark murmured, smiling with lazy triumph into her hostile face. 'For us to...entertain each other...'

'That's blackmail!' Susannah flung at him furiously, her anger only making him smile more.

'Blackmail is a very ugly word, my dear Susannah,' Mark returned smoothly. 'I much prefer—persuasion...'

Dear Reader

Here we are once again at the end of the year... looking forward to Christmas and to the delightful surprises the new year holds. During the festivities, though, make sure you let Mills & Boon help you to enjoy a few precious hours of escape. For, with our latest selection of books, you can meet the men of your dreams and travel to far-away places—without leaving the comfort of your own fireside!

Till next month,

The Editor

Kate Walker was born in Nottinghamshire but as she grew up in Yorkshire she has always felt that her roots were there. She met her husband at university and she originally worked as a children's librarian but after the birth of her son she returned to her old childhood love of writing. When she's not working, she divides her time between her family, their three cats, and her interests of embroidery, antiques, film and theatre, and, of course, reading.

Recent titles by the same author:

SHATTERED MIRROR

CALYPSO'S ENCHANTMENT

BY
KATE WALKER

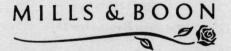

MILLS & BOON

MILLS & BOON LIMITED
ETON HOUSE, 18-24 PARADISE ROAD
RICHMOND, SURREY TW9 1SR

*MILLS & BOON and the Rose Device
are trademarks of the publisher.*

*First published in Great Britain 1994
by Mills & Boon Limited*

© Kate Walker 1994

*Australian copyright 1994   Philippine copyright 1994
This edition 1994*

ISBN 0 263 78766 4

*Set in Times Roman 10 on 10 pt.
01-9412-66613 C*

Made and printed in Great Britain

CHAPTER ONE

'I HOPE I'm not going to regret this.'

How many times had she said that? Susannah wondered, debating with herself, and trying to decide whether going back to the island was a terrible mistake. The first worrying quiver of uncertainty had started up in the moment that she had booked her flight at the travel agent's and it had nagged at her ever since in spite of her efforts to push it away from her mind by reminding herself of all the positive reasons she had for making this journey. After all, she had promised Andrea that she would be with her before the end of the month, and it would take more than the prospect of stirring up some rather unpleasant memories to make her go back on that promise.

But her certainty wavered again as she packed her case, anxiety preying on her mind all through the journey to the airport. In the bustle of the checking-in procedure she managed to forget it once more, and after that it was too late; she was committed, unable to back out—and if she was strictly honest with herself she didn't actually want to. Excitement at the prospect of travel, at the thought of leaving the dreary drizzle of a wet March Sunday in Manchester, lifted her spirits so that she positively enjoyed the three-hour flight, convincing herself that her earlier anxiety had simply been the result of stress. She was worn out by twelve months of hard work. She hadn't taken a single day off in the past year, throwing herself into her job in an effort to block out her thoughts—to forget...

But no, she resolved, stretching to ease limbs aching from the cramped confines of the plane's seats before stepping out of the stuffy cabin and into the fresh, clear, warm air, she wasn't going to think about that. It was all behind her, in the past, and she was going to leave it there. Above her head the sky was blue and cloudless, the sun, infinitely welcome after the cold damp weather she had left behind, beating down, its heat moderated by the soft breeze that lifted the short strands of her jet black hair, wafting them around her face.

All that worrying had been a mistake, Susannah told herself as she made her way towards the airport buildings. She had let things get on top of her, muddling her thoughts. What she needed was a proper break. After all, her last attempt at a holiday had proved abortive, ending abruptly as it had done, in such unpleasant circumstances. She was long overdue for some rest and relaxation.

Resolutely refusing to let the interior of the airport bring back painful memories of the last time she had been there—on her hurried flight back to England, summoned by her father's anxious phone call—Susannah made her way through Passport Control, collected her case after only a surprisingly short wait, and headed towards the main hall where Andrea had promised that someone would be waiting to meet her.

'I doubt that I'll manage to be there myself,' she had written. 'I'm still trying to get the timing of feeds et cetera right. But I'm sure that Theo could get away for an hour or so.'

But it seemed that Theo hadn't been able to make it, Susannah reflected ruefully, seeing no sign of the slim, bespectacled figure of her sister's husband. Not that it mattered; she was more than capable of making her own way to the hotel. In fact——

The thought died unformed in her mind as a movement nearby drew her attention, her gaze focusing on the man who had just straightened up from where he had been lounging against the wall on the opposite side of the hall. There was a heavy thud as her case slid from her suddenly nerveless fingers and landed heavily on the floor, the sound seeming to Susannah's whirling brain like the death knell of her hopes of any sort of relaxation as she admitted to herself that her worries had been justified after all. Worse, in fact, because she had never anticipated *this*.

'Oh, no! Please let it not be true!'

The words escaped her lips in a shocked whisper, forced out of her by the sight of the man she least wanted to see in all the world. And there was no chance of it being just a dream or a delusion; he was too real, too solid for any such hope. There was no mistaking the height and width of him, the amber brown eyes with their heavy lids that gave him a sleepily sensual look which she knew was totally deceptive, or that distinctive tawny gold hair and the all too familiar impatient gesture with which he had just pushed it back as it fell forward over his face.

'*Mark Kingston*!' she whispered in a shocked undertone.

Grimly Susannah acknowledged that her uncomfortable recollections of this man were precisely why she had felt so unsure about coming back here—though she had never anticipated his actual physical presence. She had nerved herself to face the memories that would be stirred by seeing again the places she had visited on that disrupted holiday a year ago, but she had never allowed herself to consider the dreadful possibility that Mark Kingston might be here in person.

'What the hell are you doing here?' she demanded as soon as he came within earshot, the effort to keep her voice low making her words hiss through clenched teeth, her face set in defiance and angry refutation of his approach.

'Welcome to Malta,' Mark responded with deliberate irony, his darkly sardonic tone stinging like the flick of a whip—as she was sure it was meant to. His bronze-coloured gaze met her defiant dark blue one head-on, the infuriatingly provoking gleam of satirical amusement lurking in its depths infuriating her further. 'Whatever happened to hello?'

'I have no hellos for you!'

The inner tension that was twisting her stomach into tight, painful knots made Susannah's voice sharper and more aggressive than she had intended, and she winced mentally at the sound of it, all the more so when she saw from the darkening of those heavy-lidded eyes just how her response had angered him.

'No, I don't suppose you have,' he drawled with a
dangerous silkiness, his lazy eyes dropping down from
her faintly flushed face and over her tall, shapely body
in a scrutiny so obviously assessing that Susannah was
a prey to a weak wish that she had dressed with rather
more style.

The peach-coloured, oversized T-shirt and white Lycra
leggings, worn with elderly trainers and a battered denim
jacket over the top, had been comfortable and practical
for travelling, but they were far from new and, while
normally that wouldn't have troubled her in the slightest,
if she had even suspected that she would come up against
Mark Kingston again she would have made sure that she
was looking her best, simply in order to boost her morale.
Facing him again so unexpectedly, even after a gap of
almost thirteen months, she felt she needed all the self-
confidence she could muster.

'And, as I recall, goodbyes aren't too much in your
line either.'

'Why, you——!' Susannah felt his sarcasm like the
sting of a metal-tipped whip. 'You're surely not claiming
that I broke your heart?' If he had a heart to break,
which she doubted.

'Hardly.'

If she had needed any confirmation of the shal-
lowness of his feelings, then that laconic response would
have reinforced her already low opinion of him. At least
he had dropped the seductive act, she reflected privately,
determinedly ignoring the twist of distress that told how,
even after a year, her self-esteem hadn't recovered from
the realisation of how easily he had deceived her. For a
few glorious days Mark Kingston had made her feel
special—wonderfully, devastatingly alive—so much so
that when reality broke into her dream world, bringing
home to her the truth about how basic and downright
sordid his motives had actually been, it had been like
coming up hard against a brick wall.

'But you could have had the courtesy to tell me to my
face.'

'Courtesy!' Susannah echoed disbelievingly. The truth
was that if she had waited to speak to him personally
she would have been more likely to slap his face than

give him any courteous explanation. It was because she had wanted to tell him why she had to leave so unexpectedly that she had gone to his room that morning, making the discovery that had finally stripped the scales away from her eyes, blasting her out of the blind delirium in which she had lived for the past seven days and bringing home to her just how she had been used.

'Would that have been too much to ask?' The bite of his cynicism was sharp as acid.

'Yes, it would——'

Unable to express the anger bubbling up inside her with any degree of coherence, Susannah actually stamped her foot hard enough to draw the attention of several other holidaymakers newly disembarked from the flight on which she had just arrived. And having glanced her way, three of them—young, obviously single males— paused to look more closely, much to her consternation. A moment later her discomfiture was aggravated by the audible comment, 'Very nice! I hope she's staying in our hotel.'

She wouldn't have been human if she hadn't been flattered, the uncontrollable rush of colour to her cheeks betraying her response. After all, she had never considered herself to be particularly attractive to the male sex, feeling that her rather imposing height of five feet ten inches, triangular face with strong cheekbones and slightly slanting dark blue eyes were dramatic and forceful rather than traditionally attractive in a way that the short, almost boyish cut of her straight jet black hair emphasised strongly. But just lately, with the advent of one or two of the so-called 'super-models', she had been aware of a new and very different image of female beauty, one which made her own looks appear less of an exception to the rule.

'Sorry, mate, the lady's spoken for.'

Susannah's mind hazed in shock and disbelief as she heard Mark Kingston respond to the casual compliment and saw the man who had spoken glance curiously in his direction, then, obviously taking in the other's height and imposing width of shoulder, clearly back down, lifting a hand in a gesture of resigned withdrawal.

'How dare you?' she spluttered furiously, incensed by
his arrogance, and feeling for all the world like some
disputed bone over which two dogs had faced each other,
only for one to back down when confronted by the superior size and strength of the other. 'Don't I have some
say in the matter? I'm not just a possession to be——'

'Did you want him?' Mark confounded her by asking,
cutting in on her sharply. 'You only had to say.'

To her horror he lifted his hand to draw the other
man's attention again.

'*No*!'

Without thinking, Susannah reached out and caught
hold of his arm, restraining him physically, and she was
intensely grateful to see that his mouth closed over the
words he had been about to shout, his arm lowering
slowly to his side.

'No?'

One eyebrow drifted upwards in a sardonically
mocking response and with slow deliberation he let his
bronze-coloured gaze drop to where her hand lay, slim
fingers white against the tanned skin of the strong forearm exposed by the rolled-back sleeve of his pale blue
shirt. Immediately Susannah snatched her hand away,
cursing the betraying rush of hot colour that flooded her
face.

'No——'

It was a struggle to keep her voice steady as she fought
against the floodtide of emotions that assailed her, sub-
jecting her to such a torment of conflicting feelings that
she felt as if she were on a mental rollercoaster, rushing
up, up into blazing, liberating anger one moment, then
just as swiftly plunging way down into dark unease and
embarrassment as her mind flicked back into the past,
when she had also been here, on this island, with this
man...

And all the time, unwanted and infinitely disturbing
because it was the last thing she wanted to feel, she could
not be unaware of another, very different feeling, one
that flashed along her nerves like a powerful electric
current, sparking off an instantaneous reaction
throughout her body. The feel of smooth, warm skin
under her fingertips, the hard strength of muscle that

tensed against the pressure of her grip, were too familiar to be denied—too familiar and too evocative, awakening sensations that made her snatch her hand away swiftly as if she had been burned.

And she had been burned, emotionally at least; burned so badly that she still had the mental scars to prove it. The twelve months that had passed had not been long enough to allow her to build up her defences as strongly as she had hoped; the dangerous lure of attraction that this man had held for her a year ago still had the power to reach out and touch her like some powerful elemental force so that she shivered in involuntary reaction. Last year she had barely escaped from that force with her sanity intact—what would happen to her this time if, after such a brief exposure to its impact, she was already feeling this way?

'No,' Mark repeated, giving the word a very different intonation. 'Of course not. He wouldn't present enough of a challenge for you. You'd chew him up and spit him out in twenty-four hours flat.'

Then, as Susannah struggled to find words adequate to express the anger that seemed to be rising in her throat, choking her, he reached out and took hold of the handle of her case which still lay on the ground where she had dropped it in the first shock of realisation of who he was.

'Is this all your luggage?' he enquired smoothly, bewildering her with yet another of those disturbing changes of tone.

'Yes, but I can...'

She was forced to let the rest of the sentence trail off uncompleted as, ignoring the note of protest in her voice, he lifted the bag and turned to move away. With a supreme effort Susannah dragged herself back under control. She had been thrown off balance by seeing him so unexpectedly, but she had to get a grip on herself again. She had already let him see far too much for comfort, and, knowing Mark Kingston, that was something that was decidedly risky.

When it occurred to her that in fact she knew very little about Mark—hardly more than his name and his occupation—and yet, in other ways, she knew every intimate detail about him, the sense of unease that twisted her stomach had her rushing into unguarded speech.

'You haven't told me what you're doing here.'

'I came to collect you,' Mark returned, his imperturbably smooth tone and faintly condescending smile making her feel gauche and stupid for even hinting at the question.

'I can see that!' she snapped. 'But Andrea——'

'Oh, Andrea didn't send me. Theo got caught up in some crisis at the hotel, and I volunteered to take his place.'

That would explain it; Susannah mentally apologised to her sister for thinking ill of her. She should have known that Andrea would never have sent this particular man to collect her, even if he was the only person available. Her older sister was the one person in whom she had confided anything of what had happened last year—and even she didn't know the full facts. But why hadn't Andi at least warned her that Mark was here in Malta? They had spoken to each other on the phone only last night, and she hadn't said anything then.

'I could easily have managed by myself.'

'I'm sure you could—but Andi had told Theo that you were to be met at the airport, and, as you know, whatever Andi wants, Andi gets.'

That was certainly true, Susannah admitted to herself. After all, wasn't she here, against her better judgement—a judgement that had just proved to be far more accurate than even she had anticipated—simply because Andrea had wanted her here? But then, long ago, before she had ever come up against Mark Kingston, she had promised her sister that when Andrea's first child was born she would make sure that she saw it before the baby was a month old. And as James Theodore Zammitt had been born precisely twenty-seven days ago she had only just made it in time to keep her word.

Susannah frowned slightly, recalling the telephone conversation she had had with her sister. Andrea's tone of voice, a thread of tension running through her words, had led her to suspect that all was not well in the Zammitt household and, that being so, it explained why Mark's presence on the island had not been mentioned. Andi obviously needed some sisterly support, and she would know that the mere mention of his name would make sure that the proposed visit would be cancelled until he was no longer around.

'But what are you doing *here*—in Malta?'

'Even bankers take holidays sometimes.'

Mark's response was accompanied by a slanting, side-long glance at her face, still slightly pink with indignation, and Susannah felt her colour deepen again as she recognised the deliberate reference to their first meeting, when she had asked him how he earned his living. He had told her then that he was a banker, and, with an image of the middle-aged and decidedly staid occupant of the post of manager of her local branch in her mind, she had found the description very reassuring, even if she had found it difficult to equate Mark's buccaneering good looks and strong body with the image of a conventional white shirt, grey suit and restrained tie.

It was only later that she realised how naïvely trusting she had been. She had learned the real truth from her brother-in-law, Theo.

'A banker!' he had laughed. 'Susie, Mark can only be called a banker in the same way that Richard Branson could be described as a man who owns a record store. He's a financial genius. He has a form of intuition—an instinct for investment and playing the stock market—that's nothing short of psychic. Even in these dangerous recession-hit times it's never let him down.'

'He's rich, then?' Susannah had said shakenly, and heard Theo's snort of laughter.

'He made his first million before his twenty-fourth birthday and he's gone on multiplying that by about one hundred per cent every year since.'

And as it was nine years since Mark had celebrated reaching the age of twenty-four, Susannah now told herself, his personal fortune had had plenty of time to grow to a phenomenal amount. She couldn't help wondering if he had used the twelve months or so since she had last seen him to add another fortune to the one he already possessed.

That remark about taking a holiday had been purely ironical too, she knew. Mark was rich enough never to have to do another day's work if that was what he wanted. But at heart he was still a gambler—enjoying the thrill of risking his money and his reputation—especially his reputation—on the vagaries of the market. He acted as an investment adviser also, offering his expertise to other companies or single investors, proving to have the magic touch where their money too was concerned.

Privately she doubted that he ever really took a holiday. Even last year, he had talked of the possibility of investing in property on the island, and something in his voice when he had answered her had hinted at a careful reticence, something held back—probably another major deal that he was planning.

'You've been working hard, I take it.'

She laced the words with a honeyed sweetness that revealed the gibe for what it was, deliberately letting her dark blue eyes linger on the tan that darkened the skin of his face and arms, then immediately wishing she hadn't as her mind filled with memories of how it had felt to be held in those arms, feel the warmth of that bronzed skin against her own. Hastily she lifted her gaze back up to his face, seeing from his swift grin that he was well aware of her sarcasm.

'The markets are definitely dodgy these days. You could lose a fortune in a single day if you weren't careful.'

'Always supposing that I had one to lose!' She made no attempt to disguise the sharpness of her tone now. 'We're not all multimillionaires!'

Her verbal arrow bounced straight off his thick skin, not a flicker of reaction showing in the bronze eyes behind luxuriant black lashes.

'And how is life at the leisure centre? Busy as ever?'

Not 'Are you still working at the leisure centre?' Susannah noted with a tremor of apprehension. Clearly he already knew that she hadn't changed her job since she had last seen him. The thought that perhaps he had been making enquiries about her brought a decidedly ambiguous rush of feeling, one of uneasiness mixed with a disturbing sense of flattered pleasure which she crushed down swiftly. It was much more likely that Andrea had simply talked about her job at some point.

'The recession has affected us too,' she said, the touch of stiffness in her voice the result of her seesawing emotions. 'We've lost a couple of members of staff already—made redundant on a last-in, first-out basis.'

'But your position is secure?'

They were moving now, heading towards the exit, Mark carrying her case with an ease that Susannah privately envied. Her tall build and her job as an instructor at a leisure centre, specialising in teaching aerobics and swimming, meant that she kept extremely fit and she could have managed the case herself, but she was well aware of just how heavy it was and so had to admit, unwillingly, to a sneaking sense of admiration at the way that Mark showed no sign of strain or even of making any particular effort.

'I'm safe for the moment. After all, I have been there for six years—I started when I was nineteen—and I was made a senior instructor last year.'

She prayed that Mark wouldn't hear the catch in her voice, the slight unevenness that betrayed more of the way she felt about that promotion than she was prepared to reveal, particularly to this man.

But she should have known that he was too perceptive to let her comment pass unremarked. She was subjected to a probing look from those golden-brown eyes, the scrutiny so intense that she actually flinched away from it.

'But there could be problems in the future.' It was a statement of fact; he wasn't asking her if this was so. 'This car...'

With a light touch of one hand he guided Susannah towards a sleek grey vehicle which looked slightly incongruous as it was parked among an assortment of the more usual Maltese cars, some of them appearing to have been made up from parts found in a scrap yard. They certainly wouldn't pass an MOT in England, Susannah reflected, using the thought to distract herself from the twisting pain that still accompanied any thought of the circumstances surrounding her promotion.

'Is your job at risk?' Mark persisted and Susannah responded with an inarticulate murmur which might have meant yes. 'But they've only recently promoted you.'

'Look—do you mind if we get on?' she broke in on him, hurrying round to the other side of the car and flinging open the door. 'Andi will be wondering where I am.'

She didn't want him probing into the details of her job, particularly the reasons for her promotion. She still hadn't come to terms with the fact that she now had Simon's job. In fact when she had first been offered the position she had been tempted to reject the idea out of hand, but stern realism had forced her to face the fact that, if she didn't take Simon's place then someone else would—he wasn't coming back. And so she had accepted—but that didn't mean she felt good about it; quite the opposite. She would much have preferred to be back in her original job and know that Simon still held the senior position.

'. . . don't you think?'

As if from a long way away, the sound of Mark's voice broke in on her thoughts and, coming back to the present with a start, she realised that he was now in the driver's seat and that when he spoke through the open door she hadn't heard a word he had said.

'I'm sorry.' Her voice implied that she actually felt the exact opposite. 'What did you say?'

'I simply pointed out that we would make much faster progress if you actually got into the car.' Mark's exaggeratedly reasonable tone grated on nerves newly sensitised by the distressing memories she had been recalling. 'Instead of standing there daydreaming.'

'I wasn't daydreaming!' Susannah snapped, getting into the seat beside him with more haste than elegance and slamming the door with unnecessary force so that Mark winced visibly. 'I was thinking—there is a difference!'

'But whatever you were *thinking* of put a distinctly dreamy look on your face,' he returned sharply. 'I wonder what it was—some man?'

'My thoughts are my own, Mr Kingston!' Susannah declared tightly, busying herself with the seatbelt in order to hide her face for fear it might betray how close he had come to the truth—though her expression must have been totally at variance with her thoughts for him to have described it as 'dreamy'. Nightmarish was more like it; the bitter sense of guilt never far from the surface whenever she remembered the mess she had made of things with Simon. She was thoroughly disconcerted to hear Mark's cynical laughter in response to her tart reaction.

'Not a man,' he corrected himself, his tone laced with dark acid. 'I doubt if there's a male alive who could touch that unfeeling heart of yours and leave a mark. How many poor fools have there been since me, I wonder? How many more notches on your belt, how many——'

'Bleeding hearts scattered along my path?' Susannah put in coldly, her tongue dripping sarcasm to match his own to cover up the painful sting she had felt at his attack.

Simon had accused her of breaking his heart—but no, thinking of Simon was a mistake; her unhappy memories destroyed her defences and left her vulnerable to Mark's advances. That was what had happened last year, and she had learned her lesson from what had followed.

She couldn't understand where Mark's bitterness came from—it wasn't as if he had been in the least bit emotionally involved. Did he really believe that she would still swallow the line he had spun her about being knocked for six by meeting her? Surely the way she had left, making Andrea promise not to reveal her address, had told him that his act had been exposed for the lie it was. 'Really, Mr Kingston, your imagery is a little over the top. I didn't think you went for that florid sort of style.'

'I doubt if you know anything about my style,' Mark returned levelly enough, but the narrowing of the golden eyes that stared straight ahead, a perceptible tightening of his hands on the wheel and a dark undertone to his words all warned of a dangerous temper only barely kept in check. 'After all, you didn't stick around long enough to find out.'

He paused just long enough to let that dig sink in—
or had he meant her to respond in some way? Susannah
couldn't imagine what he might expect her to say; his
words had silenced her as effectively as if he had slapped
her across the face. She couldn't believe that he had the
nerve to play the abandoned lover when she knew that
he had never intended that their relationship should last.

'And the name's Mark—we did at least get as far as
being on first-name terms before we fell into bed—or
had you forgotten that?'

How could she ever forget it? Susannah reflected, a
hot wave of anger warring with a bitter sense of injustice
at his implied accusations of being so shallow. After all,
she had simply played things his way, the way he had
made it obvious he wanted them. Was all this simply the
result of hurt male pride, piqued by the fact that she
had stolen his thunder and been the one to say goodbye,
a role he obviously had planned for himself?

'I didn't think you'd want me to use your Christian
name—not after we parted so—awkwardly.'

'That's one way to describe it,' Mark murmured,
giving the words a darkly cynical emphasis as he turned
the key in the ignition.

She was getting very tired of his accusing attitude.
'Would you believe me if I told you that I had my reasons
for leaving so abruptly?' she asked sharply.

For a moment she thought that the sound of the engine
catching had drowned her words and that he hadn't heard
her, but then, with the noise of the car dimmed to a
smoothly efficient purr, he turned to face her, bronze
eyes hooded and distant, his mouth slightly twisted in
an expression of satirical mockery.

'Oh, I'm sure you had,' he drawled with a silky nonchalance that didn't quite match the anger shown by the
tautness of muscle in his jaw. 'But I don't really think
I'm interested in hearing them.'

Susannah no longer knew which was uppermost in her
mind, the sense of injustice or the fury that was building
up to boiling point; she was only aware of the need to
wipe that condescending sneer from his face.

'There was another man——' She blurted the words
out, not pausing to consider whether they were wise.

'I rather suspected there was,' Mark broke in, his eyes hardening to freezing chips of amber ice. 'After all, you'd been faithful to me for all of—what? A week?' Susannah knew he had no need to ask; he knew every bit as well as she did just how long they had spent together. 'Seven whole days. No wonder you wanted someone new.'

'It wasn't——' Susannah began indignantly, unable to believe that he was still keeping up the pretence of the deserted lover, but he wasn't listening.

'Even for a holiday fling, that must be something of a world record.'

The bitterness he injected into the words 'a holiday fling' was the last straw. In the heated turmoil of Susannah's mind, the volcanic lava of emotion, which she had tried so hard to control, finally swelled up and erupted, swamping all common sense.

'Seven days with you was quite enough!'

Then, as those hooded eyes narrowed dangerously, some terrible demon of inspiration put into her thoughts exactly the right way to wound him most.

'I was bored!'

'*Bored*!'

For a moment the sense of pure violence which emanated from the lean body so close to hers was so strong that Susannah thought she could actually physically feel it, and she knew a painful twist of fear deep in her stomach at the thought that she might have pushed him too far. She flinched back in her seat as she saw how the strength of his fury etched white marks around his nose and mouth. She had really stung his male pride with that comment, she reflected with a stab of apprehension. But then he regained control of himself, drawing a deep, hissing breath between clenched teeth.

'Bored!' he repeated in a very different voice, an ominously dangerous tone that sent shivers of reaction down Susannah's spine, like the trickle of icy water against her skin.

Already she was regretting her foolishness, cursing the loss of temper that had driven her to fling the insult in his face. It wasn't even true—quite the opposite, in fact; boredom was the last thing she had felt. But such a response was typical of her, one her sister had often reproved her for.

'When you're *really* mad you often say the exact opposite of what you actually mean,' Andrea had once told her when calm had finally descended after one of their adolescent quarrels. 'You'll have to watch that, Suze. One day it could get you into real trouble.'

And now Susannah strongly suspected that that time had come as she tensed in her seat, nerving herself to try to retract the lie—because it was a lie—or to defend herself, and even she wasn't sure which step she was about to take.

'Then that phone call...'

So he had heard about that; very probably from Maria, the receptionist who'd taken the message, because she had made Andrea promise not to say anything about it. But Maria would have told Mark anything he wanted; she had obviously had an outsized crush on him.

'Simon...' she croaked, her voice dying in her throat as his dark brows drew together.

'Simon!' he pounced on the name like a predator on its prey. 'So that's what he's called. So tell me, Susannah. This Simon—I take it he was the man you left me for.'

Even as she opened her mouth to deny his accusation, a sudden idea struck Susannah, making her swallow down her impetuous denial and replace it with a sharp, cold little nod. She hadn't left Mark *for* anyone, but perhaps it was better for him to believe that she had. That way, she would be spared having to explain the whole sorry story to this cold-hearted, selfish man, a man who had probably never experienced any emotion even close to love in his life, and so would never understand the lengths to which his feelings had driven Simon. And surely if Mark believed her to be the sort of uncaring creature who could turn from one man to another without a moment's hesitation then he would want nothing more to do with her—which was exactly how she would like things to be.

'He called and you went running.'

Oh, that really stuck in his macho throat, Susannah reflected bitterly. In his supreme arrogance, he couldn't bear to think that she might actually prefer someone else to him! Perhaps she didn't regret that 'boring' gibe after all. It seemed to her that Mark needed taking down a peg or two—or three, or four. And she certainly wasn't going to explain that the man who had called had in fact been her father and that it was the appalling news he had given her—that Simon had been involved in an horrific accident—that had made her pack and leave at once.

'Is he still around—still in your life?'

'N—no.'

Even to score points, to knock him back—however much he asked for it—she couldn't lie about a thing like that.

'No, I thought not.'

In his anger, Mark unthinkingly pressed his foot down on the accelerator, making the engine roar protestingly, and drawing several intrigued or annoyed glances from pedestrians before he jerked it up again.

'I suppose he *bored* you too. So how long did you give him? A week like me? More? How long before you said goodbye?'

It was as if he had put a knife on a barely healed wound and pressed down hard, reopening the fragile scar. Driven beyond control of any rational thought, incapable of heeding even such feeble warnings as her subconscious was capable of forming, Susannah finally lost her tenuous grip on her volatile temper. She didn't care that he could not possibly know what had happened to Simon; was past caring what she said; needed only to hurt as he had hurt her.

'If you must know, I said goodbye to him just forty-eight hours after I left you.'

Then, hating the look of dark triumph mixed with scathing contempt which showed in his eyes, driven beyond rational thought by that terrible, final memory, she flung all caution to the winds, abandoning any attempt at self-restraint.

'But I'll tell you one thing, Mr Holiday Fling Kingston! That one night with Simon was enough to wipe every second we spent together from my mind!'

She'd done it now! Susannah reflected on a wave of something close to panic as Mark swore savagely and, with a violent, jerky movement, slammed the car into gear and swung it out on to the road, ramming his foot down on the accelerator with a ferocity that flung her back in her seat, driving all the breath from her body. If he had been angry before, then it was as nothing to what he was feeling now!

CHAPTER TWO

STILL, Susannah was forced to admit, she had only herself to blame. After all, hadn't she really been aiming for just this reaction ever since she had spotted Mark Kingston waiting for her in the airport reception hall?

Thrown completely off balance mentally by his unexpected appearance and the memories that had rushed to the surface of her mind as a result—memories she would have preferred to leave, if not buried, then at least filed away under 'U' for Unwanted—she hadn't known how to react. At first she had tried to brazen things out, pretend his being there didn't affect her at all, but she hadn't been able to keep that up. Mark's calmly satirical attitude had piqued her; and then she had been completely thrown by the way he had played the hurt, abandoned lover. She could see no reason at all for any bitterness on his part—*he* had been the one who had used her—and as a result she had been driven to snap and gibe at him, trying to make him angry enough to drop what she was sure was just a deliberate act.

Which he certainly was now! Though 'angry' didn't accurately describe the mood that gripped the man beside her. 'Furious' was more like it, the intensity of his feelings pushing him to drive the sleek dark car with a recklessness and speed that, even in Malta which had more than its share of crazy motorists, merited a few stunned glances.

Not that there was anything actively dangerous about his driving, Susannah had to admit. After the initial shock of being flung back in her seat, she had been well aware of the fact that Mark was in full control of the powerful vehicle, even on the island's winding and often pot-holed roads. Nevertheless, she wished he would slow down.

23

'Do you mind driving a little less like a maniac?' she demanded, wincing inwardly at the recognition of how tart and unpleasant her voice sounded, quite unlike her normal way of speaking.

In fact, she hardly recognised herself at all in the person she had become in the short time since she had got off the plane. Her mother, who believed strongly in manners making the man—or woman—would be shocked by the behaviour of the daughter she described as 'the sensible one', in contrast to Andrea's more impulsive temperament.

'*Please*,' she added in a belated attempt to reduce the impact of her earlier harshness, admitting to herself even as she spoke that she still sounded more sarcastic than polite.

At first she thought that Mark hadn't heard her, or, if he had, had no intention of acceding to her request. Certainly, he didn't so much as glance in her direction or show any sort of response to her request. But then, just as she was opening her mouth to repeat it, more forcefully, the headlong motion of the car slowed gradually, finally settling on a more controlled, reasonable speed.

'Thank you.'

Was it just her own sensitivity, or did her voice, even on those two short words, still have the sharp snappishness of a bad-tempered terrier? In the back of her mind she heard her mother's reproving voice and fought a sharp and uncomfortable battle with her conscience as it reproached her, adding the warning that she was risking further repercussions by such attacks.

Perhaps she had gone too far. After all, Mark had come to collect her when Theo hadn't been able to manage it. He hadn't had to do that; she should be grateful for his consideration at least. As Mark carefully manoeuvred around another car which was positioned exactly in the middle of the road, she seized her opportunity, clearing her throat awkwardly.

'I remember when Theo first warned me about situations like that. He said that officially people drive on the left on Malta except when the sun's out and then they drive in the shade.'

She was relieved to see a faint flicker of a smile cross Mark's hard face in response to her tentative olive branch.

'That's an old Maltese joke, but often it's very close to being accurate.'

Susannah was frankly astonished by the evenness of his tone, the almost relaxed way in which he replied. What had happened to the blazing fury which only moments before had been an almost tangible force, filling the confined space inside the car with a power so strong that she could almost see the electrical sparks that flashed around them? Could it really have evaporated so easily? Or perhaps, like her, Mark had decided that politeness was the wiser course.

Either way, she was thankful for the easing of the tension between them and determined to keep the peace for the rest of the journey at least. The drive to the hotel was going to be extremely unpleasant if she didn't.

'How did you come to know Theo, anyway?' she asked, curiosity overcoming her. When a small part of her mind reflected that this was the sort of question she should have asked twelve months before, bringing with it uncomfortable recollections of the other considerations which had preoccupied her then, she squashed it down hastily, refusing to let it disconcert her.

'I've known him since I was eighteen, though we lost touch for a long time and only renewed our acquaintance within the last year or so. We met at university—our rooms were next door to each other in hall. We held each other's hands in the first couple of weeks.'

'Oh, come on!' Susannah refused to be deceived by the dry humour in his voice. 'I can't believe that you ever needed your hand held by anyone! Theo perhaps, but——'

'I am human.'

His tone was rather more emphatic now, enough to make Susannah's stomach lurch nervously, fearful of a repetition of his earlier anger. As Mark brought the car to a halt at a red light he slanted a wryly mocking sidelong glance at her face.

'And I'm sure that, at eighteen, even you needed a shoulder to lean on occasionally.'

'Why "even me"?' Susannah demanded. 'Andi's the confident one in our family. She breezes through life without a care, meeting and enjoying every challenge that comes her way.'

That was why her sister had made such a success of her job as a rep for a travel company, loving every second of it until she had been posted to Malta where she had fallen in love, firstly with the island itself, and then with Theo whose family owned several of the hotels at which she worked.

'You don't do so badly in the confidence stakes, either.'

Which just proved how little he actually knew her, Susannah thought privately. She was a very different sort of character from her sister, preferring to take life as it came, not rushing at it headlong. But then the sudden recollection of the way she had behaved the previous March, when she had first met Mark, came back to haunt her.

With a shake of her head she pushed it away. Last year had been a temporary mental aberration, a time when her behaviour had been totally out of character as a result of a set of circumstances beyond her control. She had come to Malta not only to visit her newly married sister and see the magical island that Andrea raved about, but also to escape from a relationship with Simon which had suddenly developed into something that she didn't know how to handle. As a result, she had been very much off balance mentally when she had met Mark Kingston. Her mind skipped away from recalling the repercussions of that meeting. She had well and truly gone from the frying-pan into the fire.

'That doesn't happen often.' Mark's comment as the car moved forward again jolted Susannah out of her thoughts and for a moment she stared at him blankly, not knowing what he was talking about.

'What doesn't? Your being human or my needing a shoulder to lean on?' she enquired suspiciously. His comment had been threaded through with an amusement that she strongly suspected was at her expense.

'Being caught at the traffic lights.' He was definitely laughing at her now, and his amusement stung with the realisation that she had made something of a fool of herself. 'They're the only ones on the island,' he explained with exaggerated reasonableness.

'I knew that!'

Belatedly Susannah recalled Andrea telling her about Malta's one set of lights, shifting uncomfortably in her seat as she felt the emotional pins and needles which had assailed her in the first moment she had seen him return in full force.

She was having great difficulty in keeping up with the many shifts and changes in Mark's mood and his attitude towards her. In the half-hour or so since he had first approached her, he had been sardonically polite, frankly overbearing, inexplicably bitter, and apparently genuinely interested when he had asked her about her job. But that mood had then switched to barely controlled fury—under provocation, she had to admit—then back to politeness, and now she could only describe his approach as teasing. She had no idea what might come next and it was wearing her out trying to keep up with him. To add to her mental discomfort, there was the fact that she strongly suspected this was exactly what Mark intended. He seemed to have decided on a campaign of changeable, unpredictable behaviour in order to unsettle her totally—and she had to admit, however unwillingly, that he was succeeding—damn him! She had to get the conversation back on an even keel.

'There aren't many people around,' she remarked, simply for something to say.

Another wickedly glinting sidelong glance slid to her face.

'That's because it's siesta time.' The side of his mouth curled up in a smile of sardonic amusement. 'They have better things to do.'

At Susannah's hastily indrawn breath, a response she regretted as soon as it escaped her, the lop-sided smile grew, becoming a wicked, devilish grin.

'Don't you remember?' he drawled with lazy mockery.

Heat suffused Susannah's entire body, sweeping over her in waves that had nothing to do with the sun shining high in the clear blue sky. If she could have demanded that he stop the car and let her out this minute then she would have done so, she thought furiously, feeling his nearness, his very physical presence like an oppressive force, threatening to suffocate her, preventing her from breathing naturally. But they were still some miles from the hotel and her case was securely locked in the boot.

Besides, such a reaction was probably exactly what Mark was aiming for, she told herself sternly, struggling to regain control of her temper. He wanted to know that his words had affected her and if she showed her feelings then he would have won—and she was damned if she was going to let him score a single point over her.

'The heat does strange things to some people,' she retorted acidly. 'It addles the brain.' It had certainly scrambled hers.

'It was a fairly cool spring, as I recall,' Mark put in with infuriating calmness.

'For Malta!'

Susannah knew that she was clutching at straws, but she had to admit that she wasn't thinking at all straight right now. Everything seemed to be slipping from her control, like a film projected at the wrong speed, far too fast, so that all the actions blurred, becoming totally indecipherable. How she wished that she could stop it, rewind the tape and start again.

Or was she simply over-reacting to everything? Other people had holiday flings and coped afterwards without this sort of mental disturbance. But then, they probably didn't have the same personal standards as she did so they weren't left feeling that they had compromised their principles, their whole conception of themselves. At nineteen, barely out of school and desperately naïve, she had been caught in the classic 'he's only after one thing' scenario and, after finding that the rest of that saying was true—that once the man in question had got what he wanted she didn't see him for dust—she had suffered such a painful reaction that she had vowed that from then onwards sex without love was just not for her and never would be. And she had always stuck to that belief—until she had met Mark Kingston. With him, principles, guidelines, beliefs, everything that she thought made her the person she was, had gone out of the window, shocking her, once she had come round from the delirium, with the realisation of what she had done, and her self-respect hadn't yet recovered.

'But things still got pretty hot—especially at this time of day,' Mark murmured, deliberately taunting her.

The car rounded another bend, following the coast road, heading out towards St Julian's, the twisting movement making Susannah sway in her seat, leaning disturbingly close to the lean, strong body beside her. The subtle, musky scent of some cologne tantalised her nostrils and she was stunned by the instant reaction that seared through her, every nerve seeming to come alive, awakening to quivering response.

Unbidden and unwanted, memories rose in her mind, memories of those early afternoons when, as in most Mediterranean countries, everything in Malta closed down and there was nothing to do but linger over an extended lunch, laze by the pool, or retire to the cool shelter of a shuttered bedroom...

But no, she had been down that dangerous path once before—and once was quite enough. Seduced by the sun, the magic of the island, by Mark's undeniable physical attractions, but most of all by his words, she had foolishly let down her guard and lived to regret it. More potent than any of the Maltese wines, the things Mark had said had gone straight to her head, driving out all common sense, intoxicating her so that she had fallen under his spell. But an enchantment was all it had been, a pretence with no more substance than a magician's sleight of hand—and just as short-lived. The realisation that all those words had been lies, coldly, callously calculated to sweep her off her feet and into his bed—which they had done, all too easily—had devastated her in a way that now, simply recalling it, she shifted uncomfortably in her seat, feeling alternately hot and then shiveringly cold as if in the grip of some dangerous fever.

To her horror, the small movement brought those bronze eyes swinging round to her again, making the blood rush into her cheeks. It seemed that the intensity of his gaze would sear through her like a laser, seeing all that was in her mind, and her stomach clenched in panic in the same moment that, devastatingly, her heart jumped in a response that she couldn't deny, even to herself, was one of purely primitive physical awareness.

'I don't remember any cold days at all.'

Mark's tone was laced with double meaning and he deliberately lingered on the word 'cold', turning it into an almost sensual sound, one that aggravated Susannah's hypersensitive state almost beyond bearing. It seemed as if her vision had hazed so that she was completely unaware of her surroundings, the soft, peachy sand-coloured stone of the houses, the rocky coastline, the brilliant, jewel-bright clear turquoise of the sea, every sense responding solely to the presence of the man at her side.

'Are you all right?'

In the moment that Mark spoke, jolting her out of her heated imaginings, Susannah caught a glimpse of herself in the car's mirror, seeing in her sudden loss of colour and uneven breathing the reason for Mark's concerned enquiry, the frown that drew his dark brows together.

'Is something wrong?'

'I...'

She had to answer him, but when she tried to speak her voice failed her, drying painfully. Swallowing with difficulty, she ran a nervous tongue along her parched lips to ease their discomfort, her heart clenching in panic as she saw the golden brown gaze flick down and follow the small, betraying movement. She felt as if her thoughts were etched on her face in letters of fire, her response to him burning in her eyes, so that she had to struggle against a craven impulse to close them, hide from his intent scrutiny.

'I'm fine,' she managed at last, but in such an uneven croak that her declaration was totally unconvincing—and to judge by the way that frown had deepened, Mark thought so too.

'You don't sound it.'

'I am! It's just...'

Mentally, Susannah gave herself a fierce, furious shake. Get a grip! she ordered her malfunctioning brain. Say something sensible!

'It's just—the road—I feel a little unwell...'

As they had just left the coast road to head up the steep, winding hill towards the hotel, the twisting and turning necessary gave an added plausibility to her words and she knew, thankfully, that Mark had believed her as he slowed carefully.

'You should have said. I didn't realise. Hang on——'

'No—don't stop!' Susannah said hastily, realising what he meant to do.

If he parked the car now—turned to her—perhaps even touched her—she wouldn't be able to bear it. She felt as if she would shatter into a thousand tiny pieces at the slightest physical contact; every nerve in her body seeming to be rawly exposed on the surface of her skin.

'Don't stop!' she said again.

'But——'

'We're nearly at the hotel; it isn't worth the bother of parking when we're so close. I'll be fine,' she added more emphatically when he looked dubious, and was relieved to find that her voice held much more conviction than before.

'Well, if you're sure——'

'Positive.'

That sounded even more definite, in fact, it was probably rather *too* strong for someone who was supposed to be feeling car-sick.

'Just get me to the hotel—I'll feel much better when I can get out of this car.'

And that was the absolute truth, she reflected wryly as Mark put his foot down again. She would feel a hundred times better when she was out of the car and as far away from Mark as was possible. Just to be with him made her feel like a time bomb which had been programmed to explode in the very near future.

But she couldn't go on like this; she had to regain control of her emotions. If Mark was here, on Malta, then it was most unlikely that he would only be staying for a day or so. Unless she took the coward's way out, turning tail and fleeing, breaking her promise to Andrea and ruining her much-needed holiday, she would have to spend some time in his company at least, so she had better find a way of coming to terms with that fact.

Was she going to let Mark ruin her holiday for the second time in just twelve months? No way, she resolved determinedly, refusing to let herself admit that he hadn't exactly ruined the previous one—it had only been in retrospect, when she had had a chance to look at things more clearly, that the painful kickback had struck her.

Resolutely Susannah used the final few minutes it took them to reach the top of the hill and turn into the hotel's courtyard to pull herself together, gathering the scattered remnants of her self-control round her like a protective cloak. She had been thrown off balance by Mark's unexpected appearance at the airport, and he had detected her consternation and played on it, provoking and disturbing her further. Well, not any more. The worst had happened—she could cope from now on.

'Here we are.' Mark pulled on the brake and switched off the engine. 'How are you feeling now?'

'Much better, thanks.'

Susannah knew she sounded it too. Her inner determination had imposed a strong degree of control on her voice, her body, and most of all her mind. Turning to Mark with a carefully polite smile, she no longer saw a dangerous devil who was a threat to her self-control, whose very existence made her doubt her own belief in herself, but only a man with whom she had once shared a brief but intense relationship which she now knew had been a terrible mistake—one she had no intention of repeating.

'Before we go any further, I'd like to make one thing clear.'

It was strangely difficult to meet his eyes. The clear, unblinking force of that bronze gaze was too intent, too direct for comfort, so that she flinched away from it, focusing on his firm, strong mouth instead.

'And that is?'

No, looking at Mark's mouth was a mistake as well. She was too aware of its finely carved shape, the sensual fullness of its lower lip. The disturbing memory of how it had felt to have that mouth on hers was too close to the surface of her mind, waiting to bubble up again if her concentration slipped.

'About—us...'

The word caught in her throat, choking her, and, knowing that he was watching her closely, she hastily looked out of the window, staring hard at the hotel doors until they became just a blur.

'Us?'

How did he manage to get so many shades of intonation into a single syllable? Satire, mocking enquiry, scepticism, and a worrying thread of sensual approval all blended together and, although she steadfastly refused to look at him, she felt sure that that beautiful, strong mouth had curled up at the corners into a wicked smile.

'What about *us*, Susannah?' he asked softly when she hesitated, losing some of her hard-won resolve. 'Tell me.'

'About last year...' Her voice broke embarrassingly and she had to force herself to go on. 'Our...'

She couldn't find the right word. 'Romance' was totally inaccurate. 'Relationship' too deep, and 'fling' had already proved to be too inflammatory a description for her to risk using it again. Mark waited for her to continue, not saying a word, but to Susannah's disturbed frame of mind even that silence seemed to have a mocking quality about it as if it amused him to watch her struggle.

'Our affair—it was a mistake—it should never have happened.' She drew a swift, nervous breath. 'I don't want...'

'Don't want what, Susannah?' Mark prompted softly when once more she hesitated.

With an effort she made herself meet his eyes head on, though it took all her mental strength to ignore the taunting gleam in them.

'I don't want to revive it—take up where we left off. It's all behind me—forgotten...'

'Ah.' The soft sound of Mark's response seared over her raw nerves. It was obvious that its silky calmness was the exact opposite of the way he was really feeling. 'Did I suggest that?'

Fiery colour flooded Susannah's cheeks. The mild enquiry was deliberately aimed at making her feel a fool— and it had succeeded only too well. But still she was determined to make her position clear.

'Just in case you had any ideas,' she said tautly, her lips feeling so stiff that they might have been made of wood.

'I see.'

'I hope you do.' Susannah struggled to ignore the ominous softness, the deceptive gentleness of his response. 'Because I—want it fully understood——'

'Oh, I *understand*,' Mark broke in, still in that dangerously quiet tone. 'But forgive me if I don't actually agree. You may think that what there was between us is all over and forgotten...'

Susannah winced inwardly at the bite of the acid he injected into the last word.

'That might be the way you want it, but I'm afraid that my memory isn't quite as convenient as yours—it doesn't just blot out things I prefer not to recall as if they hadn't happened. *I* remember everything, Susannah.'

He let his eyes drop downwards, his cold gaze sliding over her body in deliberate and arrogantly insolent appraisal.

'I remember every last little detail—all of it very vividly. In fact, there are one or two memories I'd like to relive...'

Those hard bronze eyes moved to her mouth, lingering deliberately so that she almost felt their gaze like a soft caress before once more she was subjected to a blatantly sexual appraisal, one that made her shiver in unwilling but uncontrollable response.

'Then you can get that idea out of your head at once!' she cried sharply. 'Because, believe me, the memories you have are all you're going to get!'

She reached for the door-handle, fumbling in her haste to open the door and get out of the car, away from Mark, putting as much distance between herself and him as possible. To her furious consternation, Mark reached past her, releasing the lock with a lazy ease. But when she would have scrambled out of the open door he moved swiftly, catching hold of her arms, his grip light, exerting no pressure at all but holding her still as much by the look in his eyes as any physical constraint.

'Last year you ran out on me, Susannah,' he said darkly, his tone sending a sensation like a trickle of icy water sliding down her back. 'That's not something I'm used to—or something I like. This relationship——'

'There is no relationship! It's over—finished!' Susannah flung at him, her voice high and sharp. 'We're here together by chance—ill luck—we——'

She broke off abruptly as Mark shook his head, his expression hard and unyielding.

'You've got it all wrong, darling.' His intonation turned the term of affection into a scathing insult. 'It's not like that at all. Why do you think I'm here? Coincidence? Chance? No way—Theo told me you were coming and I just couldn't wait to renew our acquaintance.'

Susannah shuddered at the menace in his voice, a terrible sense of dread twisting painfully in her stomach. She had been right in thinking that she had hurt his pride in being the one to leave the previous year—but what could he want from her now? The answer could be summed up in three short letters—sex, pure and simple, was what he was talking about—not that there was anything *pure* about his motives! Well, she'd been easy prey for him last time, hypnotised by the glib, seductive lies that he'd told her, but she'd pretty soon been disillusioned.

Now she thought she saw just why he had persisted in playing the jilted lover at the start. He hadn't even realised that she'd sussed him, that she'd realised what he had been up to last year. Because she'd fallen into his hands like a ripe plum then, he obviously thought she would do exactly the same this time. Well, he'd better think again.

'No——' she began, but Mark wasn't listening.

'We're here together because that's the way I want it,' he went on, a hateful note of triumph, of cruel satisfaction, making her want to put her hands to her ears to block out the sound. 'I don't like unfinished business——'

'It is finished! It's all over——'

'Not to my way of thinking—from where I stand, there are more than a few loose ends that need tying up. But this time I'm calling the shots—and you won't get a second chance to run out on me. This time, unless you want to risk the consequences, you stay until things are finished—and that, my darling Susannah, will be when *I* say and not before.'

CHAPTER THREE

'DON'T be ridiculous, Suze! I can't do that!'

Andrea's voice was tight with exasperation.

'I can't possibly tell Mark to go home—he's Theo's partner, for heaven's sake. He has every right to visit whenever he wants——'

'But does he have to be here *now*—when I'm here?' Still shaken as she was by the confrontation in the car, the full import of her sister's words didn't register properly with Susannah. 'Did you have to invite him——?'

'I didn't invite him,' Andrea put in. 'He doesn't need an invitation, not when he'll soon own more than half of this hotel—and all the others.'

'He—what?' Susannah prayed that Andrea hadn't said what she thought she had. 'Mark and Theo——'

'Are partners—with Mark as the majority shareholder. Or they will be once things are signed.'

'But I thought that Theo's father——'

'He retired.' Andrea's tone was weary. 'And not before time, if you ask me. He'd really let things go; almost everywhere needed repairs and modernisation. Some of the buildings aren't even safe. Theo's been on at him to do something for years but the old man was totally set in his ways, with the result that the hotels have become so badly run down that, without a lot of work, they won't reach the standards demanded by the British travel companies—and you know how Malta relies on British tourists.'

'But Theo never said anything——'

'He wouldn't——' Andrea's laugh was shaky '—and he wouldn't let me tell anyone either. This is Malta, Suze—it's still a very macho country. Theo would rather die than admit to you that he was having any problems.'

'And you can't afford to do the work yourselves?'

37

Even as she spoke, Susannah knew that the question didn't have to be asked. Theo would never consider letting another man buy shares in his family's business if he had any alternative.

'Not a hope.' Andrea shook her head emphatically. 'The recession's really hit us hard; bookings are way down. We still have to support Theo's parents, and now, of course, there's Jamie...'

She sounded very low on the last comment, making Susannah frown slightly. Andrea had mentioned something about some tensions between herself and her husband but, still reeling from Mark's declaration of intent, she had to admit that she hadn't taken much notice. Now her conscience reproved her sharply. It seemed that her instincts had been right when they had picked up her sister's distress over the phone last night.

'Last year, when Theo was in London for a couple of days, he bumped into Mark by accident—they hadn't seen each other for years. They went for a drink together, and Theo let slip some of his problems. When Mark showed an interest in investing in the business, it seemed like the answer to our prayers, and we invited him out here to look things over.'

'So that was why——'

'Why he was here last Easter?' Andrea nodded. 'You must have wondered why such a wealthy man was staying in a small family hotel.'

She hadn't even considered it, Susannah had to admit, though she should have done. There were so many questions she should have raised about Mark but, foolishly, had left unasked.

'It's taken a lot of discussion and sorting out, but at last everything seems to be falling into place and even Theo's pa has come to see that we desperately need the money Mark's investment will bring. Oh, Suze——'

Andrea caught hold of her sister's arm, the strain of the past year or so showing on her face, making her look worn and tired in a way that Susannah, used to the carefree, confident Andi, found particularly upsetting.

'It's been such a worry, especially with the baby and everything. At one point I was sure that Theo was going to go bankrupt—so Mark's been our saviour. I just hope that nothing goes wrong now; I couldn't bear it if it did.'

'But surely now that Mark's——'

'Nothing's signed yet. We won't be able to relax until it's all finalised and legally binding. But you're right—Mark wouldn't back out now.'

But suddenly Susannah found herself listening, not to her sister, but to an echo in the back of her mind where once again she heard Mark's hard voice declaring, 'This time, unless you want to risk the consequences, you stay until things are finished.'

What consequences? At the time, she had taken his veiled threat to refer simply to herself, but that had been before she had realised just how Mark Kingston held Andi and Theo's future in the palm of his hands. Was this contract and the all-important injection of cash into the ailing business what he had meant? A cold, sneaking fear slithered down her spine, making her shiver involuntarily. He couldn't! He wouldn't—would he?

Even as she rejected the idea, another memory surfaced, that of Theo describing the man who was now to be his business partner.

'Mark's always been a solitary individual—never a pack animal. Even at university he was like that and, from what I hear, in the financial world he's regarded as something of a lone wolf, someone who always hunts alone. That's how he got his reputation. If Mark Kingston wants something, he gets it—no one else gets a look-in.'

Susannah could have wished that her brother-in-law had used a less vivid description. The thought of Mark Kingston as a ruthless, solitary predator was infinitely disturbing to her peace of mind. And on a more personal level she had experience of the sort of cold-blooded heartlessness of which he was capable. Mark Kingston had wanted her, and he had set himself determinedly to achieving that aim. Not knowing the sort of man he was, she had foolishly let herself be taken in by the way he had claimed to be as stunned by their response to each other as she was. It was only later, when she had realised that she had not been special to him at all, that he had simply been looking for someone—anyone—with whom to while away a few pleasant sunlit hours, that she had seen how little it had meant to him. He had simply singled her out as the wolf Theo had described would isolate some foolish sheep as its prey. Now she shuddered to think of that stony-hearted ruthlessness being turned on her sister and her husband.

'So you see why it's important to keep Mark sweet,' Andrea was saying, her words aggravating Susannah's already disturbed frame of mind. 'Theo would never forgive me if I messed things up now. Really, Suze—is it as bad as you think?'

'Bad,' Susannah echoed hollowly, her thoughts still on the ominously threatening note in Mark's voice. But then, seeing her sister's worried frown, she hastily tried to hide her concern. Andrea already had more than enough on her plate. 'It's difficult,' she amended carefully. 'Andi—you know about last year...'

'Oh, I know you fell head over heels for him—and who could blame you? Mark's one glorious hunk of a man. If I weren't so happily married, I could go for him in a big way myself. He only has to look at a woman with those come-to-bed eyes and——'

'Andi, I did *not* fall head over heels!'

Susannah did not want to hear a detailed account of all Mark Kingston's female conquests and the ease with which he had seduced them. It made her feel even worse to know that she was just one in a long list of women who had succumbed to his particular brand of potent but untrustworthy sexual appeal. And she didn't need to be told how successful his approach was—she had had personal experience of it, at the cost of her self-respect!

'Looked like it to me,' her sister commented drily.

'That wasn't how it was! I wasn't thinking straight—as you know—and I...'

She hunted for an alternative to the 'fell' Andrea had used, thinking that that had too many emotional undertones for her liking.

'I blundered into a——' what was it Mark had called it? '—a holiday fling. It didn't mean anything—it was just a—temporary insanity—the result of stress—and when I came to my senses I realised what a mistake it had been, so now——'

'Now you don't want to see him again. After all, the point about holiday flings is that they're supposed to end when the holiday does. You aren't supposed to meet the other person again—it never works. So you feel uncomfortable with him; I can understand that.'

Uncomfortable hardly described it, Susannah reflected ruefully. Harassed was more like it; and the dreadful suspicion that Mark might use Andi and Theo's situation against her just wouldn't go away.

'But, Suze, it was more than twelve months ago; surely you're over the worst now. I can see that meeting him again like that must have been embarrassing——'

'I wished the ground would open up and swallow me!' Susannah said feelingly.

'I'll bet!' her sister laughed. 'But you're both adults— can't you put it behind you? It is past history, after all.'

But it wasn't just past history, that was the trouble, Susannah reflected miserably. For some private reason, Mark was determined to bring the whole thing right into the present.

But she couldn't tell her sister about that. Andrea saw Mark as the answer to all her prayers, a knight in shining armour who had come to the rescue in time of need. She couldn't disillusion her, particularly not when she wasn't absolutely sure of her facts. After all, Mark might not have been thinking of the contract, she told herself, acknowledging ruefully that that argument didn't even sound convincing. For his own private reasons, Mark wanted her to stay—and what better way to ensure that she did than to use his own power to make or break her sister's future as a weapon against her?

'Come on, Suze!' her sister chided, seeing her glum face. 'This isn't like you—you're normally so sensible.'

Sensible. Susannah echoed the word in her own thoughts. It was certainly the description her parents and friends often applied to her, and most of the time she supposed that it was fairly accurate. But it hadn't been at all appropriate last year. Then she had behaved crazily, foolishly, downright irresponsibly.

Perhaps if she hadn't been so on edge, so ill at ease after the way that Simon had behaved, then she might not have been so susceptible to Mark's charms. And he *was* charming. Even now, free from the madness that had gripped her when she had first met him, she couldn't deny the irresistible pull of magnetic attraction that seemed to radiate from every pore in that tall, strong body. But if her life had been on a more even keel when they had first met, then she was sure that he would never have knocked her so completely off balance that she had lost all sense of judgement. In other circumstances she was sure that she would have handled things very differently, but she had come on holiday in the first place to escape from the situation with Simon.

Simon. The other man. Susannah's lips twisted slightly as she recalled how she had spoken of him to Mark. She hadn't told the exact truth then. Simon hadn't really been the man after Mark, he had been the one before him—and the reason she had come to Malta in the first place.

'Poor Sue.' Andrea's tone was sympathetic as she intuitively sensed the direction of her sister's thoughts. 'You don't have much luck with men, do you? First, that idiot Simon——'

Susannah's head came up in surprise. 'Simon loved me—he wanted to marry me—and I hurt him so very badly.'

'He made your life hell.' Andrea dismissed her concern with an impatient gesture.

'I handled things badly—I should have let him down more gently. After all, everyone thought we were perfect for each other.'

'But you knew he wasn't right for you—and I don't see how else you could have handled it. You were honest with him—it was his problem if he couldn't accept it. Instead he hounded you, made your life a misery—I saw the results, remember,' she added when Susannah was about to protest. 'You were a nervous wreck when you arrived here last year.'

'I know,' Susannah admitted. 'I just had to get away— things were really on top of me. Simon never left me alone, and because we both worked at the same place I couldn't even escape from him there. In the end I couldn't even think straight...'

'That was why I was glad to see you spend time with Mark—at least he put a smile on your face.'

'He certainly gave me something else to think about,' Susannah admitted wryly. 'He made me forget about Simon—for a time.' And she had been so desperate to escape, to forget, that she hadn't been able to see through Mark's lies, had swallowed the stories he had spun her like some gullible schoolgirl.

'You don't regret not telling Mark about it?'

'We never had that sort of relationship. At the beginning I just didn't want to talk to *anyone*—I couldn't even think, let alone put my feelings into words. Then, later...'

Later, just as she had begun to think that perhaps she could tell Mark, open up a little about Simon and her worries about him, she had come up against the first chinks in the perfect idyll they had shared, the first hints that what Mark said and how he actually felt were two very different things.

'It never seemed to be the right time. We only had seven days, Andi.'

'But don't you think it would make things easier now, if he knew?'

Briefly Susannah reconsidered her earlier decision to leave Mark in ignorance of the true reason for her sudden departure the previous year, but almost immediately resolved to let things continue as they were. If he knew she had been forced into going by events beyond her control, then he might interpret that as meaning that she had been reluctant to leave him—which was not at all what she wanted him to think. Far better that he should go on believing that she had simply grown tired of their affair and gone back to England. After all, it came close enough to the truth. Once she had realised how selfishly he had used her, she hadn't been able to get away from him quickly enough. Simon's accident had simply meant that she hadn't been able to tell him so to his face.

'No,' she said firmly. 'The less Mark and I have to do with each other, the better.'

'Pity.' Andrea sounded positively regretful. 'I would have liked the idea of Mark as a brother-in-law, and Theo——'

'Come off it, Andi!' Susannah exclaimed sharply, unable to hide her disbelief. 'There was never any chance of that. Mark made that very plain.'

'Oh?' Andrea looked surprised. 'I thought he was very taken with you——'

'In one way only,' Susannah retorted, Mark's 'Let's just enjoy this while we can' sounding inside her head. 'I was just a holiday bonus to him—the sex to go with the sun and the sea.'

It was impossible to keep the bitterness from her voice. The discovery that, in spite of his claim to the contrary, Mark had come to Malta looking for a holiday affair had only added to the distress she had already been feeling at a very difficult time, and it was one of the reasons why she had gone so quickly, making Andrea promise not to give him her address.

Would she have felt better if he had been open about his intentions from the start? she couldn't help wondering. At least that would have meant that he was being straight with her. It was his dishonesty that had hurt most; the fact that he had fed her all those flattering, seductive lies while all the time he had been cynically manipulating her emotions.

'Oh, well,' her sister went on, 'as I see it the only thing you can do is forget about both Mark and Simon and get on with your holiday.'

Andrea made it all sound so simple, Susannah reflected later as, alone in her room, she started her unpacking. If only she really could forget. But she had never been able to get Mark Kingston out of her mind throughout the past twelve months, even when she had no idea where he was or what he was doing, so how on earth was she supposed to do it now, when he was here on the island, staying in the same hotel as she was?

Wearily she rubbed at her temples where a headache was beginning to build up, probably as a result of the emotional seesaw on which she had found herself ever since she had first set eyes on Mark at the airport. She had some painkillers somewhere...

Too much on edge to bother hunting through her handbag to find the tablets, Susannah simply up-ended it, emptying its contents out on to the bed, giving a small, hollow laugh as, along with everything else, the book of crossword puzzles which she had bought to occupy herself on the plane tumbled out on to the white cotton bedspread. It had been a shared passion for solving crosswords which had brought her and Mark together in the first place, she recalled.

It had been on her first day in Malta, when, as she had done today, she had arrived during the siesta time. Desperate to get out into the sun after bleak months spent in a typically English winter, she had abandoned her unpacking until later and hurried outside to the pool, stretching out on a lounger, and attempting to concentrate on the puzzle in the paper she had brought with her.

But the truth was that it was a pointless exercise. She was still too tense, her mind full of the problems she had left behind. It seemed to her that in the past couple of months her whole world had been turned on its head, and with it her conception of who she was.

She had always believed that love was a slow-growing progression of feeling, that it came naturally from friendship, developing and intensifying as you got to know the other person better; and she had been firmly convinced that she had found such a relationship with Simon. Like everyone else, she had believed that marriage was on the cards, and so it had come as a shock to discover that, when Simon actually proposed, her immediate response had been to feel that something was missing, something so vital and important that it was as essential to her future happiness as breathing was to her continued existence. The reaction had been on such a primitive and intuitive level, so strongly in contrast to her normal way of thinking, that she had found it almost impossible to convey to Simon, all the more so when, refusing to accept her rejection of his proposal, the man she thought she knew had suddenly been transformed into a frightening, disturbing stranger, someone who hounded her day and night, begging her to reconsider and telling her his life would not be worth living if she didn't.

The letters danced before Susannah's eyes. She couldn't make sense of the clues, let alone think of any answers; all she could think of was Simon's accusation that she had broken his heart, his demands to know why. The trouble was that she couldn't answer that, even to herself. She had thought that all she wanted was affection, support and commitment, that she didn't believe in the sort of grand passion Andrea had declared had made her leave her home and country for Theo's sake, and yet, when Simon had offered her exactly that, she had felt something close to panic instead of the contentment she had anticipated.

So what now? What did she want if not what Simon could give her? What was this thing called love? Was she even capable of feeling it? And, more immediately, how was she to get her life back on to its former calm and steady path when it seemed to have been blasted way off course, even her satisfaction in her job destroyed by Simon's behaviour? She had hoped that by coming here to Malta, by physically distancing herself from him, she would make him realise that she had meant it when she had said that she couldn't marry him, and, hopefully, accept it. If he didn't, then she didn't know what she would do—she might even have to consider leaving the leisure centre, she thought despairingly, flinging the paper away from her with a despondent sigh.

'What are you stuck on?' a low, pleasant voice had asked, making her jump like a startled cat. Absorbed in her thoughts, she hadn't heard anyone else approach.

'I'm sorry. What did you say?'

Eyes the colour of clear honey met her startled gaze, and looking deep into them Susannah suddenly felt as if her whole body was bathed in a warm glow that had nothing to do with the heat of the sun. She couldn't look anywhere else, couldn't bring her mind to focus on anything other than those golden eyes and the smile that lit them.

'I wondered if I could help. What clue was giving you such trouble?'

'Oh—ten across...'

Susannah gave a number at random, still unable to think straight. But then as he reached for the paper, glancing down at the puzzle, the hypnotic spell of those amazing eyes was broken and she found herself coming back to reality, blinking like someone woken from a deep sleep.

'Strings attached.'

'Pardon?' His words made no sense, and Susannah frowned her confusion. 'Strings?'

'Ten across—the clue is "Conditions marionettes have", two words, seven letters and eight—strings attached.'

'I see...'

His hair was a singularly attractive colour, she found herself thinking, studying it as his head bent over the paper, noting the gleam of gold and copper mixed in with the brown, shining where the sun caught it.

'And that makes seven down hindsight—oh, I'm sorry...'

The bronze head lifted suddenly and she was treated to a flashing smile of megawatt brilliance.

'This is your paper and I'm filling in all——'

'Be my guest.'

Susannah tried to sound as offhand as possible, hoping that he would get the message that she just wasn't interested. Her brain had started to function again and she felt rather foolish as she realised, belatedly, that she was in fact being chatted up. Stunned for a moment by the mesmeric force of those beautiful eyes, she had let her guard drop when she should have slapped him down from the start. Simon's behaviour had left her feeling emotionally battered and bruised. She needed time to withdraw into herself, guarding her privacy. She hadn't yet sorted out the problems her previous relationship had caused. The last thing she needed was some holiday playboy—however stunning—coming on to her.

But he *was* devastatingly attractive; she would be all sorts of a liar if she tried to deny that fact. In spite of herself, she couldn't stop her gaze from wandering over the strongly carved face before her, taking in his appearance fully for the first time, registering the impact of the fine mouth, strong jaw, and high cheekbones. He had a forceful, truly masculine beauty, she acknowledged inwardly, schooling her face to show none of her thoughts.

'If you'd like the paper, help yourself. It isn't really mine—I found it in the foyer and just brought it out for something to look at. It's yesterday's, anyway.'

'It would be,' he laughed, showing white, strong teeth, startling against his tanned skin. 'The English papers don't arrive until around four o'clock, if then. Still, at least they do get here. Theo would be quite lost without his copy of *The Times*.'

'Theo...'

Surprised by his use of her brother-in-law's name, Susannah studied the man before her with more open curiosity. That Tartar's face had a body to match, she realised, registering straight, wide shoulders and a broad chest, which narrowed to a slim waist without an ounce of spare flesh around it. He was wearing only an old pair of denim jeans cut down to make shorts, and had obviously been on Malta for some time as his long, muscular legs shared the same depth of tan as his face.

Working in a leisure centre as she did, Susannah was well used to seeing strong, highly toned bodies, both male and female, around her every day. She and her friend Rachel often joked that Mr Universe himself would have to work hard in order to impress connoisseurs such as they. But this was not the body of a man who worked out for show, to develop muscles in the right places and hold off a middle-aged paunch. This man's physique was that of a natural athlete, toned and tightened by regular exercise, whipcord-strong with its lean and elegant lines the result of a deeply ingrained and long-lived fitness. After all, even Simon, who had worked at the centre for five years, hadn't——

But no, she wouldn't think about Simon. She had come here to escape from him and the pressures he had put on her. Running away, he had called it, and perhaps he was right, but she had got to the point where she dreaded the thought of going in to work, where her heart started to race if the phone rang in case it was Simon, and so she had had to get away before she cracked up completely.

'You know Theo?' Was he just trying to impress her with his use of the hotel manager's first name?

'Yes, we—oh, I'm sorry...'

Once more she was treated to that wide, flashing smile, its warmth making her toes curl in the same second that her heart lurched into a new and accelerated beat.

'I should have introduced myself. My name is Mark Kingston—I'm a friend of Theo's.'

Unconvinced, Susannah surveyed the bronzed, strong-fingered hand he had held out to her, absently noting the immaculately clean and beautifully shaped nails, the square tips to the fingers and the complete absence of any signs of manual work. They were almost too perfect, rather like the man himself. But then, from the back of her mind, came another thought, one stunning in the intensity of its sensuality, as she considered what it would be like to feel those hands on her body, to know their caress, let it awaken every sense to glowing life.

'Really?' Thoroughly disconcerted by the burning eroticism of her thoughts, she retreated behind the protection of a stiff, unwelcoming expression, displaying frank scepticism about his claim. 'I don't recall seeing you at the wedding.'

If he'd been there, then she would definitely have remembered. If she had ever seen it before, that face would have been impossible to forget.

'Ah, well——' Mark's smile was disturbingly disarming, particularly when she wanted to keep her distance '—we're not that close—though I have known him for some time. I met him again by accident a couple of weeks ago, and, as I'm considering the possibility of investing in property on the island, he and Andi invited me to stay with them.'

'Andi', Susannah noted; and her sister had mentioned that there might be another guest.

'And you're Susannah. Andi told me to look out for you. You're not very alike, are you?'

'Hardly,' Susannah murmured, thinking of her sister's smaller, curvier figure. Andrea had inherited their mother's build, her light brown hair, while her own tall slenderness and more dramatic colouring came from her father.

'But she was right when she described you as a real beauty.'

'Oh, come on, Mr...'

She deliberately hesitated as if unable to recall his name, even though it was perfectly clear in her mind. Deep inside she knew that she was trying to deny, even if only to herself, the effect he was having on her, which was all the more disturbing because it was so unexpected. After the way her relationship with Simon had turned so terribly sour, she had felt as though every emotion in her had been deadened, her mind and her heart so numbed by the battering they had received that she couldn't respond to any man, and quite frankly she had been glad of that lack of feeling. Until she could grow a protective skin over the raw nerves exposed by the tensions of the past few months, she was too vulnerable, too unsure of herself, to cope with any other entanglements. And so it came as a shock to find herself so aware of Mark Kingston. It was also the last thing she wanted. Until she got herself sorted out, men, even lethally attractive men like this one, were a complication she could well do without.

Unfortunately, Mark didn't rise to the bait, obviously being well aware of the put-down for which she was aiming and equally clearly determined not to let her get away with it, his golden eyes surveying her taut face with a calmly knowing smile that told her he knew exactly what she was up to.

'I doubt that Andi used the word...'

For some reason the syllables of 'beautiful' seemed to stick in her throat, warm colour flooding her cheeks as he let one eyebrow drift upwards in amusement at her hesitation, his smile growing into a wicked, and frighteningly attractive, full-scale grin.

'OK, so she said you were a tall, striking woman,' he conceded lightly. But then, just before she could relax, he confounded her totally by adding, 'Beautiful would be my choice of description—one I think any man with blood in his veins would agree with.'

The golden gaze that now moved over her slim body was so warm with sensual approval that Susannah imagined she could feel it burn her where it rested. Her head was swimming and she was suddenly a prey to the most irrational feeling that the turquoise and white one-piece swimming costume she wore, which had seemed perfectly suitable—even modest—when she had tried it on in her room, had now shrunk by at least two sizes so that it barely covered her, and it was all that she could do to resist a craven impulse to reach for her towel and hide behind it. Only the realisation that he would know exactly what she was doing, and the interpretation he would put on her reaction, stilled her hand and forced a false smile on to her face.

'And I suppose she also told you that I needed cheering up,' she went on, recalling her sister's declaration that what she needed was taking out of herself, 'so you decided that, in that case, flattery was the best way to get what you want——'

'She told me nothing of the sort,' Mark returned with disconcerting swiftness. 'She simply told me that you were here on holiday. *Do* you need cheering up?'

The unexpected question, the way he had pounced on her revealing slip, totally disconcerted her, and as she struggled to think of a possible answer he spoke again, with an even more disturbing undertone shading his voice. 'And what, precisely, is it that I'm supposed to want?'

'Andi seems to think that I do—need cheering up, I mean . . .'

Susannah found that she couldn't meet those golden eyes. Her heart was still thudding uncomfortably and there was a dryness in her throat that had nothing to do with the heat of the sun.

'But I'm afraid that she's got it quite wrong. I don't need anything—except some peace and quiet.'

She had meant the last comment to sound emphatic but instead her voice came out unnaturally high and tight, destroying what little was left of her composure. Why did this man have such an effect on her, seeming to fuse her brain so that she could no longer think clearly or even speak at all naturally? After those months of numbness, it was as if the effect of some emotional an-aesthetic had worn off, leaving every nerve rawly ex-posed, and with all the feelings that had been blocked off now rushing through her in a raging torrent.

'So...'

Her voice failed her, her lips painfully dry, her whole body seeming to be afflicted by painful pins and needles so that she shifted uncomfortably on the sun-lounger, only to feel even worse when she saw from the faint smile that curled his mouth up at the corners how the small movement could have appeared to be deliberately pro-vocative—which was not what she intended at all.

'So you see, Mr Kingston,' she went on hurriedly—no point in pretending she couldn't remember his name any more; it hadn't worked the last time, and she could tell from the gleam of amusement in his eyes just what a fool she'd make of herself if she tried it again, 'I'd really prefer to be left on my own.'

Not true, her conscience reproved her even as she spoke. She hadn't felt this awake, this *alive*, for a long time. But it wasn't a comfortable way to be. She felt too sensitised, over-stimulated, as if every nerve in her body was responding to some sort of electricity that flowed from this man. She had never experienced anything like it before; it was a million light-years away from the way she had felt with Simon, in the beginning at least, before things had started to go wrong. Then she had felt warm and comfortable, relaxed; now she felt a prey to a form of pins and needles in every cell.

'When you've answered my question.'

'Question?'

It sounded like the squawk of a startled hen, and Susannah cursed her nervous response when she heard herself. Mark Kingston hadn't moved an inch; he was still sitting on the edge of another sun-lounger, long legs stretched out in front of him, those strong hands still holding the newspaper and pen, and yet she suddenly felt that he had come far too close, that his powerful body was towering over her, overwhelming her.

Those golden eyes seemed like deep, deep pools of warm honey, drawing her in, so that she was aware only of him, of the glow of that intent gaze, the shape of his mouth, the way his chest rose and fell as he breathed, the gleam of the sun on his tanned skin, the soft lift of his hair in the faint breeze. Her own body flushed with warm response, her breathing quickening, growing shallow as her blood seemed to heat in her veins until she felt sure that its colour must show through her transparent skin.

'What question?' she managed again, her voice hoarse.

Don't play games. He didn't have to say the words; they were implicit in the wickedly gleaming glance he shot her from under those lazily drooping lids. But she *wasn't* playing at anything. The truth was that she honestly couldn't remember what he was talking about. What *had* he said earlier? She couldn't think—it seemed as if the heat in her body had hazed her mind, like spectacles or a car windscreen fogging up as a result of the warmth of one's breath.

'Just what is it that I'm supposed to want from you?' Mark's tone made the words sound light, but there was no matching amusement in his eyes, which were as hard and intent as ever, and this time he did lean closer, so much so that she caught the faint, musky scent of his body, an essence more potent than any perfume she had ever smelt before.

'I...'

There was a buzzing inside Susannah's head like the sound of a thousand angry bees, and the only coherent thought she could form was one that turned her rigid with shocked disbelief.

She wanted to touch this man—wanted it more than anything in the world! She wanted to feel the warmth of his skin beneath her fingertips, let her palms slide over the muscled contours of his shoulders and chest...

Ruthlessly she forced her wanton thoughts back under control, exerting a determination that made her head reel, had her leaping to her feet in a rush of panic, her action indicative of her inner rejection of the sensuality of her thoughts. The stress she had been under had affected her more than she had realised. She had never felt like this about any man in her life before, let alone one she had only just met and knew nothing about!

'I don't know what you want, Mr Kingston, but you certainly won't get anything from me! I want nothing from you, and I have nothing—nothing at all—to give you—now, or at any time in the future.'

And then, because she couldn't bear to be close to him any longer, because those amber eyes seemed to be boring into her skin, burning the delicate flesh, because the heat that suffused every inch of her body was too much for her to bear, she spun round on her heel, flinging herself away from him, and plunged into the nearby pool in a desperate attempt to calm her racing pulse.

CHAPTER FOUR

'SUSANNAH! Suze—are you in there?'

The sound of her sister's voice calling her name intruded into Susannah's thoughts, giving her almost as much of a shock as that moment when, twelve months before, forgetting that the hotel pool wasn't heated, she had plunged into the chilly water, and for a second or two she found herself actually gasping aloud.

'Suze! Are you OK?'

'Yes——' With an effort Susannah found her voice and the energy to get to her feet, moving to answer Andrea's knock. 'I'm fine.'

That was not strictly true, and the faint quaver in her voice revealed as much. Simply recalling her first meeting with Mark had revived the physical tensions, the febrile rush of heat through her body, the sense of shocked disbelief that had assailed her then, so that now she felt weak and shaken, as if she had only newly recovered from some feverish illness. She was sure that her feelings must show in her face, something that was confirmed when, as she opened the door, her sister gave her a suspicious, shrewdly assessing look.

'Just what have you been up to?'

'Nothing!' Still shaken by her physical response to what were, after all, only memories, Susannah had to work hard to make her voice sound firm and even. 'I've just been unpacking.'

'For this long?'

Andrea was openly sceptical, and her eyebrows lifted pointedly as her gaze swept over the suitcase that lay, still half full, on the bed.

'Really, Suze, you're here on holiday. Any normal person would have got this done long ago and be out enjoying the sun.'

'And I will—just as soon as I'm ready.'

55

Her control hadn't been as strong as she would have wished, and Andrea frowned her concern.

'You're not still fretting because Mark's here, are you—hiding away from him? Look, he won't make any waves, I'm sure of it. He's really a very nice guy—honest.'

'Nice' wasn't a word she would use to describe Mark Kingston, Susannah reflected. Dangerous was definitely closer to the truth—disturbing—downright threatening. *'Devastating'*, her mind threw at her with shocking unexpectedness, and she knew that she couldn't deny it. He was fiendishly attractive, and her response to him earlier had shown that the sexual magnetism which had been her downfall last year hadn't died but still lingered like a banked-down fire which smouldered slowly, needing only the smallest puff of air...

Her mind flinched away from contemplating the possible consequences, and, suppressing a shudder of reaction, she forced herself to smile at her sister.

'I'm sure he is.'

'But if it really bothers you, I suppose I could say something...' Andrea's doubts about her own suggestion were obvious. 'But I don't think Theo would like that——'

'Of course you mustn't do that!'

Her earlier worries had been the result of tiredness and the stress of seeing Mark so unexpectedly, so that her imagination had been working overtime, she told herself. They had to be; Mark hadn't specifically mentioned Andi and Theo, or the difficulties the business was in; she was worrying unnecessarily.

'Don't worry about it, Andi. Mark and I were just a holiday fling that burned itself out.' She was pleased to hear that her voice held a credible note of conviction. 'I was embarrassed at first, it's true, but that's all over now.'

A fling was what Mark had called it, she recalled bitterly, and to him that was all it was. *He* wouldn't have experienced that sense of shock which had rocked her belief in herself with the realisation that she had behaved like a tramp, subject to a wild force that had taken over completely, subjugating all her principles to a passionate need that was like wildfire raging out of control. And that was something he must never know about or she would never be able to face him again. It had been hard enough to rebuild her shattered self-respect the first time; if Mark ever suspected that she hadn't been able to handle their affair as casually as he obviously did, then what was to stop him using that against her?

Andrea's relief was obvious, a smile wiping the tension from her face so that Susannah was glad that she had made the effort to appear unconcerned. Her sister really did look tired and overwrought; the last thing she needed was any further dissension in her home.

'If you could just bring yourself to be polite...'

And that, of course, was the answer, Susannah reflected on a rush of relief. She would be perfectly polite to Mark, supremely, impeccably, unremittingly polite—so polite in fact that he wouldn't be able to fault her behaviour in any way, wouldn't be able to raise objections to any action she took without making himself look a fool, and if *he* made any hostile moves, then he would inevitably put himself in the wrong in everyone else's eyes. She would be so damn polite that he would know it was an insult but wouldn't be able to do anything about it.

'Oh, yes,' she said firmly, a gleam of triumphant anticipation in her eyes. 'Yes, I can manage that.'

She was rewarded by Andrea's wide smile of gratitude.

'It'd mean a lot to me, Sue. If this contract is signed then Theo will be able to relax...'

'Don't worry about a thing,' her sister assured her. 'It's quite often the case that husbands feel a bit neglected with a new baby in the house, and if Theo's had money worries too, then it's no wonder that you've both been feeling decidedly uptight. But you're on the home run now; it won't be long before the partnership agreement's signed and all your problems are over. And if my being polite to Mark Kingston will help things run smoothly—well, I promise you I'll do everything I can.'

The only problem, Susannah reflected some time later when they had all gathered for dinner, was that it seemed that Mark, too, had decided on a similar ploy to her own, so much so that if she hadn't been feeling so apprehensive, on Andrea's behalf as much as her own, she would have found the situation extremely funny. The aggressive, threatening character of the drive back from the airport had suddenly been transformed into a perfect, supremely courteous gentleman who poured her drink, held her chair for her when she sat down at the table, and made light, easy conversation that covered the awkward silences she occasionally lapsed into as she struggled to adjust to this new persona.

Susannah's resolution to behave as if nothing had happened had faltered slightly when she had first entered the room to find Mark already there, dressed in pale linen trousers and a milky coffee-coloured long-sleeved cotton T-shirt, his cool elegance reminding her forcefully of the physical impact he had had on her the year before, and she had to struggle to match the air of relaxed social ease which he exuded so effortlessly, hiding every trace of the darkly dangerous man who had so disturbed her earlier.

'You must see more of the island this time.' Theo, who seemed totally deceived by the other man's act, apparently oblivious to any emotional undercurrents in the present situation, was blithely unaware of any possible dangers in his words. 'You hardly went anywhere on your last visit.'

'I—yes...'

Susannah didn't know how to answer him, painfully aware of the way Mark had turned his head in her direction as Theo spoke.

'Yes, you must,' he drawled softly and, unable to stop herself, Susannah glanced in his direction, meeting head-on the undisguised dark amusement at her discomfiture that gleamed in the amber eyes. 'It would be a waste of a trip otherwise.'

'Susannah had other things on her mind last time,' Andrea put in, meaning to be helpful, but causing her sister to come close to choking on her wine as she saw Mark's mouth curl up at the corners.

He knew only too well just what had kept her at the hotel, in her room or his, on her previous visit. Was he now recalling, as she was, the long, sensual hours spent

locked in each other's arms, the drugging physical
pleasure of their lovemaking that rendered them insen-
sible of their surroundings or the passage of time? Her
blood began to burn in her veins at the thought, and she
took another hasty gulp of her drink in an effort to
quench the fire that was building up inside her.

'I—wasn't in the mood for sightseeing.'

'I understand that. But, as Mark says, it would be a
waste not to see more this time. You're lucky, you'll be
here for the Easter celebrations. You missed them last
year. I think you'd be interested in the Good Friday
procession.'

'Yes, I would.'

Susannah struggled to make her response sound
natural. She was supremely conscious of Mark sitting
opposite her, his long body relaxed, leaning back in his
chair, tanned fingers curled round his wine glass. His
head was still turned in her direction and she knew that
he was watching her closely, could almost feel his tawny
gaze fixed on her face, bringing a wash of warm colour
to her cheeks.

What was going through his mind? she wondered. Had
he, like her, been recalling the embarrassing details of
her previous visit, or was he thinking of something else
entirely? The real problem was that she couldn't decide
whether she would feel a wonderful sense of relief if the
latter was the case, or a bitter twist of pique at the
thought that she could be so easily forgotten.

'It's a pity that Andrea's tied down with young Jamie,'
Theo went on, 'otherwise she could have shown you
round.'

It was the perfect opening, Susannah acknowledged
with a terrible sense of dreadful inevitability twisting in
her stomach as she waited for Mark to make the obvious
response, knowing just what he would say.

'I could do that.'

It was perfectly pitched, every shade of intonation
carefully controlled, the easy smile, the swift glance in
her direction—a glance which, if you didn't know the
true facts, could be seen as one of warm invitation. But
Susannah did know the truth, and so found it impossible to meet that bronze gaze with any degree of

equanimity, fearful of the mocking gleam she would see, the cynical amusement that would destroy her already uncertain self-control.

'Oh, I couldn't possibly trouble you,' she said hastily, wincing inwardly at the sound of her own voice. Politeness was one thing, but that had been verging on obsequiousness. It wouldn't get her off the hook either, she admitted, realising too late that she had left herself open to only one possible response which, of course, was precisely what she got.

'No trouble at all,' Mark returned smoothly, infuriatingly sounding much more convincing than she had been able to.

He was matching her at her own game—matching her and then outstripping her—Susannah thought angrily, forcing herself to keep her expression bland and smooth, not daring to risk the furious glare she longed to direct at Mark's smugly triumphant face.

'I think that's a great idea,' Theo put in. Clearly he was determined to keep his potential business partner happy, she realised, signalling frantically to her sister with his eyes, wanting her to intervene.

But Andrea simply lifted one hand, fingers outspread in a gesture of defeat. After all, if Mark was to become the majority shareholder then he would be investing a very large amount of money, and with the deal currently in its delicate final stages, neither Theo nor Andi would want to put a foot wrong.

'No, really, I couldn't impose on you.'

She was beginning to feel desperate now. She wanted to shout, to fling angrily in his face the declaration that she wouldn't tour the island with him if he were the last man on earth, but she had resolved to be polite, for Andi's sake, and although the words stuck in her throat, polite she would be, even if it killed her.

'It wouldn't be an imposition—I volunteered.'

He really was a master of the art of insincere pleasantries, Susannah reflected bitterly, shocked to find that, just for a second, even her resolve was weakened by the charming smile which accompanied the smooth words, swayed by the way it seemed to light up his whole face. She had never realised just how good an actor Mark

Kingston was—which forced her to reconsider other, equally apparently sincere moments, and remember, with that sense of nausea rising in her throat once more, that she had been as badly fooled then as Andrea and Theo seemed to be now.

'But you must have seen all the tourist sites——' She had to force the words out from lips that suddenly seemed to have turned to wood, becoming awkwardly stiff and unyielding. 'You won't want to visit them again.'

Then, seeing from his expression that he was going to refute that statement—ever so politely of course—she rushed on hastily, 'I can manage by myself—use the buses. They're cheap and——'

'And crowded, and often uncomfortable,' Theo put in. 'After all, most of them are ancient. They were given to the island when they'd been retired from use in England and some of them date from the fifties at least. You'd find life a lot easier in a car—and if you don't fancy driving yourself...'

In spite of her efforts to hold it back, Susannah couldn't hide the shudder of apprehension that shook her at the thought of venturing on to the chaos of the Maltese roads. She was a nervous enough driver on the routes she knew at home, and as far as she could see the only thing that made driving on Malta even remotely like the experience in Britain was that, officially, they were supposed to keep to the left.

'I'm well used to the conditions here,' Mark took up the argument once more. 'Besides, the buses aren't always convenient. I don't think they'd be the best way to get where you want.'

So now he was claiming to know the places she wanted to visit! Irritation welled up inside Susannah, wearing down her resolve to keep to strict politeness so that her eyes flashed with annoyance.

'And where would I want to go?' It was a direct challenge, furious blue gaze clashing with lazily amused amber one. He couldn't possibly know—not unless he was a mindreader.

'Mdina?'

Mark's response was deceptively mild, with a faint questioning note lifting the single word at the end, giving it a surprisingly diffident sound, almost as if he were unsure of himself. But that was just more acting; she had forgotten how, in an unguarded moment last year, she had revealed that the ancient city was the place on Malta she most wanted to see. Her irritation grew as she saw how, as Mark realised that she had remembered, that faintly mocking smile had widened into an infuriatingly taunting grin.

'Mark's right.' Andrea's interjection covered her sister's disconcerted silence. 'If you wanted to get to Mdina from here you'd have to go into Valletta first and then get a second bus from there. It would be the same on the way back. It would take ages.'

Et tu, Andrea? Susannah thought, turning a baleful glare on her sister, her mood only aggravated by the fact that she knew Andi was right. But all the same, she was supposed to help her get out of this situation, not provide further arguments to back up Mark's suggestion.

'And if you wanted to know the background of the place you couldn't do better than to have Mark as your guide.' Theo took up the other man's case once more. 'He knows even more about the history of Malta than I do.'

He would, Susannah thought furiously, feeling irrationally that Mark might almost have swotted up on the story of the island simply in order to block off one more escape route. Now she could no longer declare that she would rather visit the ancient town on an organised trip, with a guide who could tell her all about it.

'Of course, if you don't want to visit the Silent City...'

Mark really deserved an Oscar for his performance, Susannah admitted, grudgingly acknowledging an unwilling admiration for the way he managed to sound both nonchalantly indifferent and suitably disappointed at the same time.

'Oh, no—it's one of the places I most want to see. Mdina has always sounded so magical—so mysterious...'

At the tiny quirk upwards of the corners of his mouth she cursed her impulsive declaration. Her unguarded tongue had betrayed her, leading her straight into his carefully laid trap, and she hadn't even seen it coming. It was probably the effects of the wine: she had forgotten that the Maltese vintages had a higher alcohol percentage than most.

'Then you'll accept my invitation?'

She had been manoeuvred into a corner, Susannah was forced to admit, beaten at her own game by a master. Her resolve to be polite had checkmated her completely. If she behaved in a hostile manner now she would lay herself open to accusations of being unfair and unreasonable, just as she had originally planned that Mark would be, and even though Theo had always seemed to be the mildest and most polite of men, she was sure that if she rebuffed his prospective partner's apparently courteous invitation then he would take it as something close to a personal insult. She had promised her sister that she would do everything she could to help, so now she was trapped.

With a sense of desperation she tried one last approach.

'But wouldn't it spoil your visit to have me tagging along? I mean, wouldn't you rather visit Mdina on your own?'

'On the contrary,' Mark returned smoothly, making Susannah grit her teeth against an angry outburst as he persisted in the careful politeness which had so infuriated her. 'I'd be glad of the company. After all, I doubt very much that you have ever just "tagged along" with anyone. And besides . . .'

He paused to give his words deliberate emphasis, slanting a wickedly glinting sidelong glance at her flushed and indignant face.

'It would greatly enhance the pleasure of the trip—to see a beautiful city in the company of an exceptionally lovely woman.'

As Susannah struggled to think of some way to respond to that, the sound of a wail was relayed over the intercom that connected the living-room to Jamie's bedroom, alerting them to the fact that the baby was awake and hungry. Immediately Andrea got to her feet and headed for the door, followed a few moments later by Theo, his colour slightly raised.

'Nappy duty,' he muttered, obviously in some embarrassment, addressing his partner.

Mark's laugh in response was surprisingly warm.

'Your sister has Theo well trained,' he commented as the door closed.

'I think it's very important that a father should do his share of looking after a baby,' Susannah responded stiffly, still painfully aware of the way he had outman-oeuvred her.

'I couldn't agree more,' Mark disconcerted her by saying. 'It takes two to create a child, after all, and a baby can only benefit from having the love and care of both parents.'

Just for a second, his voice altered, touched with a note that made her wonder if he spoke of something more personal. But when he continued it was as if the tiny moment had never been.

'But I understand that Theo's father's thinking on these matters is practically prehistoric and he is quite shocked by Theo's domesticity.'

'As he is by the sale of shares in the hotel business.' The words slipped out before Susannah could catch them back. Mark shot her an unnervingly sharp, assessing glance.

'You know about that?'

'Andi mentioned it.' It was a struggle to keep her voice calm, not to betray her inner tension. 'She says that you're here to sign the final contracts.'

That bronze-eyed gaze slid away from her for a moment to focus on a point on the horizon beyond the window where the sea met the darkness of the night sky.

'That was the plan,' he murmured enigmatically, his tone and the use of the past tense making Susannah's heart lurch painfully, all her fears reviving in a rush.

'Was?' It came out in an uncomfortable croak. 'There's a problem?'

'A complication.'

Still he wouldn't look at her, and she felt her nervous-ness grow because there was no way she could read his thoughts in his face.

'What sort of complication?'

At last his head turned, those cold, eagle's eyes burning into hers.

'You,' he said curtly.

'Me!'

It was an inelegant squawk of panic, leaving her with no hope of hiding her reaction from him. Her heart was racing frantically, and she knew he was well aware of her agitation, his hard-eyed gaze dropping to the rapid rise and fall of her breasts under the green silk of her dress. The threat she had tried to dismiss as simply her imagination now reverberated over and over inside her head with the force of a physical blow to her skull.

'You can't mean...' The words dried on her tongue, her voice failing her completely.

'What can't I mean?' Mark queried with dangerously deceptive gentleness.

'If I don't agree to...'

Susannah found it impossible actually to form the words 'take up where we left off', opting instead for something less inflammatory.

'You want me to stay—and this contract with Theo— his and Andi's future—is the price of my agreement.'

She would have been all sorts of a fool to expect him to look embarrassed, or even shamefaced at having his bluff called, and certainly no hint of either emotion crossed his face. After a momentary pause, which she was sure was deliberately aimed to disconcert her, he leaned back in his chair, smiling with lazy triumph into her hostile face.

'I want you to stay here and spend some time with me,' he murmured, still in that dangerously soft-toned voice. 'And Theo wants me to stay until the final problems in the agreement have been ironed out and the contracts signed. It seems an eminently satisfactory way of achieving both ends if we were to use the time to...entertain...each other.' A deepening of his voice combined with a wicked curl of his lips to leave Susannah in no doubt as to just what sort of 'entertainment' he had in mind.

'That's blackmail!' she flung at him furiously, her anger only making him smile all the more.

'"Blackmail" is a very ugly word, my dear Susannah,' Mark returned smoothly. 'I much prefer—persuasion.'

'Well, I don't!' Susannah snapped back. 'An ugly word for ugly behaviour! Don't try to disguise what you're doing by hiding behind a screen of lies!'

Her voice was high-pitched and harsh, betraying too much of her inner distress. In the moment that Mark had revealed his hand, bringing home to her that the threat she had tried to persuade herself was only imagination was in fact the weapon he planned to use against her, a sharp, stabbing pain in her heart had forced her to face the fact that foolishly, weakly, in some private, vulnerable part of her mind, she had hoped for the impossible, had wanted her suspicions to be unfounded. Now even that pathetic, desperate hope had been taken from her.

'So now,' Mark continued, his tone unbelievably light and relaxed, so that, hearing him, no one would ever have suspected that he had just made it painfully plain that her brother-in-law's financial future—and, with it, the happiness of her sister and their baby son—rested on her answer, 'how do you feel about a trip to Mdina tomorrow?'

I won't! Susannah thought rebelliously. I can't—not even for Andi! But even as the thought formed in her mind she knew she couldn't risk the consequences of acting on it, which left her with only one possible answer. But then, she consoled herself rather desperately, what could possibly happen on a tour of a historic city? Surely not even Mark Kingston could fling himself on her in the full gaze of the public.

'You've—persuaded me.'

She forced her voice into carefully decorous tones, knowing her words to be totally at odds with the impotent defiance that blazed from her eyes. The dark satisfaction that she saw in his face almost destroyed her, but she drew on years of her mother's discipline, reminding herself of her resolve to be polite—if it killed her.

'And if your invitation still stands, then I accept.'

She had no other choice, she told herself, no choice at all. But it was as Mark smiled in response to her acceptance, his golden eyes glowing warmly, his whole face lighting up, that she felt her heart lurch in a disturbing blend of pleasure and fearful apprehension, sending a rush of blood through her veins, sensitising every nerve in her body, so that she was forced to rethink the situation and wonder whether it was Mark she had to fear most or her own response to him.

CHAPTER FIVE

'I CAN see why they call it the Silent City—it's almost eerie.'

Susannah's voice was hushed to the sort of tone one adopted when in church, which was something close to the feeling which the ancient city of Mdina inspired in her. With its high, steep walls and narrow, almost deserted streets where cars were forbidden, she felt strangely as if she were in some huge cathedral. The air of mystery and withdrawal from the bustle of the twentieth century was enhanced by the fact that several of Malta's old aristocratic families lived here, their palaces hidden away behind ornate, carved doors.

'Though "city" is perhaps something of a misnomer.'

'On Malta, this is a city,' Mark returned drily. 'It used to be the capital until the Great Siege of 1565 when the Turks attacked the Knights of St John. That's when the Grand Master de la Vallette decided a new town on the coast would be more easily defensible and made plans to build Valletta.'

He knew his stuff, Susannah admitted. If it was the history of the island she wanted, she certainly wouldn't have done any better if she had gone on one of the organised tours she had considered.

'So how come you know so much about this place?'

For the first time, curiosity overcame the reticence imposed by unease and uncertainty that, until now, had made her keep conversation to a minimum, offering only the most trivial and mundane comments. Not that her near-silence had caused any problems. Mark appeared once again to have set himself to be pleasant and approachable company, and during the journey from St Julian's to Rabat on the outskirts of Mdina, where they had left the car, he had provided an easy flow of information and entertaining anecdotes about the countryside through which they were driving which would have been a credit to any experienced tour guide.

'When I first met Theo—all those years ago when we were both at university—I visited him once during the summer vacation. I fell in love with the place and set myself to finding out everything I could about its history—the Knights of St John, the attacks by the Turks, and, of course, the terrible battering the island received during the Second World War——'

'That was when Malta received the George Cross, wasn't it?' Susannah asked, recalling the story Theo had told her.

Mark nodded soberly.

'Britain's highest award for civilian courage—and they deserved it. Valletta was devastated by merciless bombing and people had to take to caves to hide where they lived in near-starvation conditions. Did you know there's a church in Mosta where, in April 1942, a bomb fell through the dome during Mass and slid across the floor to the altar without exploding? One of the waiters at the hotel was there at the time with his parents and he still believes it was something of a miracle.'

'I'll bet he does! He must be thankful to be alive. It makes such a difference, you know!' she added impulsively.

'What does?' Mark asked, a puzzled frown creasing his forehead.

'Your knowing so much—it's as if you understand the true heart of Malta, not just the tourist bits.'

'Oh, if that's what you want, I'll take you to the temples at Hagar Qim or Mnajdra——'

'*Where*?' Susannah was intrigued by the names; the Maltese language was almost totally incomprehensible and she had had only the faintest idea of how to pronounce most of the island's place names.

'Hagar Qim,' Mark said more slowly, making it 'Hah-jahr-kheem'. 'That's where the famous fat lady figure was found. The temples there date from around 3000 B.C.'

'I'd love to see them.'

Susannah didn't try to hide the enthusiasm in her voice. If this morning was anything to go by, then visiting

the ancient temples with Mark to explain and inform her
would be a fascinating experience—from a historical
point of view at least. She didn't know how she felt from
a more personal perspective, the feeling that twisted in
her stomach not quite panic, though it came close, but
more a sense of nervous exhilaration that tied her in
emotional knots in a way that she felt was decidedly
dangerous.

'Is that fat lady the goddess that Andi says must have
been created to provide hope for slimmers everywhere?'
she asked hastily, trying to distract her thoughts from
her worrying response. 'The headless figure with huge
rolls of fat round her stomach and great piano legs that
I've seen on so many postcards in the shops? I suppose
that prehistoric people had a very different view of female
beauty.'

'Almost certainly she represented fertility and that's
why she had such a lush figure,' Mark agreed. 'In those
times they accepted that women should have a few
curves; they didn't have the twentieth-century fixation
with dieting to the point of emaciation.'

His remark was accompanied by a swift glance at
Susannah's own slim figure, the suggestion of disap-
proval in it enough to spur her into indignant response.

'And just what is that supposed to mean?'

'Mean?' Mark turned those golden eyes on her indignant face, opening them wide in an expression of
innocence that didn't fool Susannah for a second.

'Are you implying——?'

'I'm implying nothing,' Mark cut in on her angry outburst, his smiling nonchalance infuriating her further.
'If the cap fits...'

'I don't diet!' Blind fury drove all logical thought from
Susannah's brain, her earlier ease in Mark's company
destroyed by her indignation. Irrationally it piqued her
savagely to think that he didn't consider her attractive—
illogically so, because, if challenged, she would have said
that she didn't care what he thought of her, that in fact
she didn't want him to find her in the least appealing—
so why should it bother her now to find that he thought
the exact opposite? 'I just work off all I eat at the leisure
centre. But you think I'm too thin...'

Her voice failed her, all anger evaporating swiftly at the thought that her present slimness was the result of more than the daily activity involved in her job. After Simon's tragic accident, she had been unable to eat properly for weeks, sorrow and a terrible sense of guilt destroying her appetite so that the weight had dropped off her, and she had only recently begun to regain her natural shape.

'You said that,' Mark returned with the same infuriatingly imperturbable calm. 'But you have to admit that you've lost weight since last year, and, personally, I don't think it suits you.'

'Nobody asked your opinion,' Susannah snapped, painfully aware of the way her response was coloured by the knowledge of the reasons behind her weight loss, the recollection of the way she had thrown herself into her work with a new and excessive intensity, driving herself to the point of exhaustion in an effort to exorcise the distress that she felt, erase the bitterness of her memories, both of him and Simon. 'And besides, I haven't lost all that much!'

'No?'

Mark lifted one eyebrow in lazily sardonic query, his head tilted slightly to one side, considering bronze eyes challenging her impetuous declaration. Then, still holding her mesmerised, and moving so slowly that he deceived her into a foolish lack of suspicion, he lifted his hands and let them rest lightly on her shoulders, brown against the pale yellow of her T-shirt.

'Feels like it to me,' he murmured softly, strong fingers closing over delicate bones, gently probing the hollows near her neck before they slid slowly and sensually downwards. 'There's definitely a lot less of you...'

His voice sounded almost regretful, its low tones strangely hypnotic, combining with the heat of the sun and the soothing caress of his hands to create a disturbingly liquid weakness in Susannah's body, turning her bones to soft wax, hazing her mind.

In the silence of the deserted street she could almost hear the slow, heavy pounding of her heart as the stroking hands lingered at the curve of her hips, then, even more slowly, more seductively, reversed their

movement and began to drift upwards again to cup the
sides of her breasts, the heat of his palms burning into
her so that Susannah flicked out a nervous tongue to
ease parched lips.

'You're not the woman you used to be,' he told her
huskily, his golden gaze fixed on the small betraying
gesture.

Susannah's head was swimming; she didn't know
where she was. It seemed as if her mind had entered a
time-warp and she was back in the past, the touch of
his hands triggering images in her mind that were definitely X-rated. Beneath the hard warmth of his hands
her breasts tingled, aching for his more intimate touch,
and a devastating sense of something uncoiling deep
inside her made her want to moan aloud.

'This isn't the body I knew—and loved—before...'

The pause between the two phrases was quite deliberate, drawing out the latter into a sensual word that was
almost a physical caress in itself and, lifting one hand,
Mark let a finger trail down the side of her face, his eyes
darkening, holding her captive with just a look, so that
she couldn't find the strength to resist as his tawny head
lowered, his mouth coming down on hers.

The kiss was very light, very gentle, just the merest
brush of his lips, but the effect on Susannah was as if
she had been struck by a bolt of lightning. Her heart
jerked in her chest, lurching into a frantic pounding that
made her blood race through her veins, making her head
swim as if she were prey to a debilitating fever.

But it seemed that it had no such effect on Mark who,
far from seeming in any way moved by the caress, calmly
lifted his head and subjected her to another coolly arrogant survey, frowning his displeasure as he did so.

'I don't like what you've done to yourself——'

The critical comment jarred, jolting her sharply from
the trance, her head snapping back, breaking that mesmeric hold.

'How dare you?'

Susannah jumped away from him as violently as if she
had been scalded, and in fact her skin burned painfully
where he had touched her as if she had been out in the
sun too long.

'What the hell do you think you're doing?'

Coming back to herself in a rush of devastating embarrassment, she belatedly became aware of the fact that they were in a public place, looking round anxiously, thankful to see that the narrow, shady street was in fact deserted—something which did nothing to appease her outraged sense of propriety and self-preservation.

'Keep your hands to yourself, you animal!'

She spat the words into Mark's face, so incensed that she actually stamped her foot hard and lifted her hands, the fingers balled into tight fists as if she would have struck him, the temptation to slap the mocking look from his face almost irresistible.

'I won't have you pawing me!' She refused to let herself think that her anger was addressed as much at herself as at him, at the realisation that, with those memories, her body had betrayed her by recalling things she desperately wanted to forget—recalling them and enjoying them. 'It disgusts me!'

'That isn't how you felt last year,' Mark put in, his very quietness silencing her as effectively as a slap across the face. For a moment she almost suspected that he had been able to see into her mind and read the shameful eroticism of her thoughts. 'As I recall, you didn't describe my caresses as "pawing" then. You seemed to like them—even begged for them.'

'*No!*'

It was a shaken gasp, desperately denying his words even as the unfulfilled ache in her body brought home to her the bitter truth of them. In spite of herself she felt her clenched hands uncoil and, spreading in a defensive gesture, come up before her face. The cool shadows of the street, formerly welcome after the heat of the sun, now seemed much more disturbing, almost threatening, with the realisation of Mark's height and strength, and she suddenly felt very vulnerable and alone.

'No?' Mark echoed the single syllable, and Susannah felt that never before had she heard the simple word laced with such darkly biting cynicism. 'So now you're a liar as well as a coward, are you?'

'C-coward?'

It was all she could manage because, deep down, no matter how much she might long to, she knew she couldn't refute his accusation of lying. She *had* wanted his kisses and caresses in the past, had wanted them every bit as much as he had claimed. She had needed, had longed for his touch, opening to it sexually in a way that she had previously thought herself incapable of, feeling empty and bereft when she was alone, her body yearning for his lightest touch, driving her almost to screaming point without it.

And the real problem was that that yearning hadn't died as she had thought; it had simply been sleeping. Last night, lying alone in the darkness of her room, away from the sensual assault that Mark subjected her to simply by existing, she had convinced herself that she could go through with this visit, that Mark's presence on Malta would be no problem to her because she was over her infatuation with him—and an infatuation was all it had been. She had been mentally knocked off balance by the stress of events, the pressures Simon had subjected her to, and, weak and vulnerable as a result, had fallen victim to the sort of wild, crazy behaviour that was totally uncharacteristic of her. But it *had* been only temporary, and she was over it now.

But her foolhardy conviction had soon proved to be pathetic and unfounded, built on a treacherous quicksand instead of solid ground. It had taken only one brief caress—no, not even that, Susannah forced herself to admit, because there was no way she could describe Mark's insulting physical survey of her body by so flattering a name. There had been a coldness about it, an almost analytical quality that had turned it into an *invasion*, rather than anything more appreciative. But even that unfeeling touch had stirred her sleeping senses, bringing them awake to quivering response in reaction to the feel of his hands, the brush of his strong fingers, even in so impersonal, so calculated a way.

Was she really so weak, so much a victim of her own primitive, basic needs that even though she felt nothing for this man, even when the recollection of the wild, unbalanced lust they had shared filled her with a terrible sense of shame, he could ignite desire in her so appallingly easily?

'I'm not a coward!'

'Oh, but you are, sweetheart, you're a craven coward.' Susannah flinched at the bite of acid in Mark's voice. 'You're running scared—running away from what happened, refusing to admit to how it was——' his tone deepened, grew huskier, golden eyes burning into her, holding her paralysed when she would have pulled away '—how good——'

How it could be again. The unspoken words seemed to hang in the warm air around them; she could almost read them in his eyes, in the curve of his lips.

'Susannah——'

As he spoke, Mark reached out to her once more, but the touch of his fingers on the exposed flesh of her arm was too much for Susannah to bear in her present sensitised state.

'No!'

With a violent defensive movement she flung off his hand, swinging round and hurrying—almost running— away from him, not looking where she was going, heedless of the direction she was taking in her haste to get away from him.

For five, perhaps ten minutes she was moving blind, not caring where her steps took her, but Mdina was only a tiny place, its narrow, high-walled maze of streets leading her round in circles, eventually bringing her back to the small, sunny square in front of the cathedral.

And there, as her sense of panic and outrage slowly receded, Susannah paused to draw in several deep, slightly ragged breaths, feeling her racing heart slow and return to its normal rhythm, and as she did so she became aware of the tall, tawny-haired figure standing in the shadow of a side street, observing her. So Mark had followed her and was watching every move she made, his eyes narrowed against the sun. For a moment she was strongly tempted to march up to him, fling her anger and open defiance into his face, possibly with the slap which she had barely resisted a short time before, but then, almost immediately, she rejected the idea in favour of another, more subtle approach.

If Mark wanted to follow her, then let him! She had been foolish to let him get to her as badly as she had; the only way to handle things would be by behaving perfectly normally. That way, she would demonstrate quite clearly her indifference to his presence, which she was sure would have more effect than open defiance. After all, she had come here to see the beauties of Mdina and that was exactly what she was going to do. Fired with a new determination, she firmly turned her back on the silent, watchful figure at the corner of the square and headed for the huge, carved wooden doors of the cathedral.

Once inside, she immediately felt the cool, ageless serenity of the place enclose her and had no trouble directing her concentration on to examining every richly decorated inch of the church, admiring the marble mosaic floor, the wooden carvings, and a fresco of the shipwreck of Saint Paul, who, legend had it, had been washed up on the shores of Malta. But in spite of her absorption, her still heightened sense of awareness made it impossible to ignore the silent, distant figure of the man who had followed her into the old building.

But, strangely, all sense of danger, all feeling of threat had left her now. As long as he kept his distance, she could tolerate his presence, she told herself. In fact, as the morning drew to a close, she came to miss his company—or, at least, the knowledgeable and often witty commentary he had provided and without which she knew she was missing so much. And so when Mark finally approached her again she was decidedly more receptive than she might have been earlier, in fact, almost welcoming.

She had left the cathedral by then, and was in one of the small, dark shops—holes in the wall, Andrea called them, with their narrow doorways and windows designed to keep out as much as possible of the fierce summer sun—examining a display of Maltese lace work when he came up behind her, soft-footed on the stone floor.

'Everywhere will be closing up for the siesta soon—so how about lunch?' he asked, his voice low-toned and with a nonchalant ease that amazed Susannah. It was as if their confrontation had never happened, as if his insolent caresses, his accusations of cowardice, had all been just figments of her imagination.

'I'm not all that hungry.'

Susannah made herself put the stiff, unapproachable note into her voice. She didn't want Mark to think that she was easily swayed, forgiving him without hesitation. The sound of his voice, coming so close that she could almost feel his breath on her skin, made the tiny hairs on the back of her neck lift in apprehension, and shivers of reaction feathered down her spine so that she could almost believe that she could still feel the path his caressing fingers had taken earlier, as if it were etched into her skin.

'But I know a place where they make the best chocolate cake in the whole world,' Mark responded in a huskily cajoling murmur, one that was disturbingly seductive and tempting.

Susannah's mouth dried and she swallowed hard to ease her discomfort. In spite of her efforts to restrain them, her thoughts slipped back to the day twelve months before when the two of them had spent a long, sunny afternoon by the pool, lying on the sun-loungers, totally relaxed, just talking, the fires of passion temporarily banked down. Throughout the long, languorous hours they had been content simply to let time drift by, allowing their exhausted bodies the time to let the need, the searing desire, build up slowly inside them again. Some time earlier she had confessed to an incurable, hopeless addiction to anything chocolate, and during that afternoon Mark had fed her with pieces of *kwarezimal*, a Maltese Lenten sweet made of chocolate, ground almonds and honey. And now, hearing his enticing whisper, she felt she could almost taste again the rich sweet melting in her mouth, the chocolate smooth against her tongue.

'Well? Can I tempt you?'

The serpent in the garden of Eden must have spoken in just that soft, seductive way, Susannah thought hazily, struggling against the drugging sensation that took possession of all her senses, his honeysweet tones hiding his wicked intent. Indeed, if she were Eve, she strongly suspected that she would give in to him on anything he asked.

And was she going to allow herself to be tempted now? Would she let herself be seduced into accepting his company once again, in spite of all the warnings of her own better judgement? She would do better to reject him now, once and for all. Anything less was only laying down trouble for herself in the days ahead.

But she was dependent on Mark for transport back to the hotel, unless she were going to endure the lengthy, bumpy and hot bus ride back to Valletta where she would have to change for St Julian's. And she *was* actually hungry, she discovered to her surprise; the idea of chocolate cake was suddenly very appealing.

After all, she reasoned, she had told herself that she would match Mark's approaches with careful politeness. Defiance had got her nowhere, rudeness was churlish and counterproductive, and, considering her situation, possibly even downright dangerous, and besides, she had only just admitted to herself how much she had enjoyed his company—as a guide at least. She wanted him to tell her more about this island and its fascinating history, and he was unlikely to do that if she antagonised him.

'The best in the whole world?' she questioned archly, keeping her voice as light as possible as she swung round to face him, her heart lurching slightly as blue eyes met bronze.

'The very best,' Mark assured her, matching her tone almost exactly. 'If you don't agree, then I'll pay a forfeit—and the view from the café is every bit as spectacular as the food,' he added, offering this further enticement with a smile that in its stunning warmth would have melted a much harder heart than she possessed.

If he was going to keep things on this light-hearted, almost flirtatious level, then she was sure she could handle anything.

'Then lead me to it!'

CHAPTER SIX

'YOU were right about the view.'

Susannah gesticulated with one hand, waving it towards the expanse of plains and hills spread out before her.

'It's breathtaking—marvellous! Is that the sea away in the distance? And what's that huge dome—a church?'

'That's Mosta—the place I was telling you about. That's the dome the bomb fell through.'

'I didn't realise that it was so close.'

'On Malta nowhere is far from anywhere. If you want, we could visit it on the way home.'

'I'd like that—oh, look, here's our cake.'

Susannah eyed the rich, dark concoction with delighted anticipation.

'It looks wonderful—the culinary equivalent of the view.'

'And it tastes every bit as good as it looks.'

Mark cut off a small piece and speared it on to his fork, holding it out towards her.

'Try it.'

Looking deep into those tawny eyes, Susannah found it was once more as if time had slipped away and she was back in the previous year, when reality, sanity, everything apart from this man had ceased to exist. Her breathing seemed to stop, her heart coming to a standstill inside her chest, and she was held mesmerised, like a rabbit hypnotised by the lights of an oncoming car.

But then the waitress returned with a tray of tea, and with the clatter of cups and saucers the spell was broken so that it was as if a film which had frozen into stillness suddenly began again, her heart starting up in a rush, its rhythm fierce and uneven so that she felt the blood pulse through her veins, pounding like the sound of the surf on the shore. With an awkward, nervous gesture she repulsed the cake still held out to her.

'No—you have it. I have plenty of my own. I don't want to get fat.'

Too late, she recalled his disparaging comments on her lost weight, the darkening of his eyes telling her that he was thinking of exactly the same thing, and immediately regretted drawing his attention to the issue once again.

'The architecture of this place always amazes me,' she began hurriedly in an attempt to distract him. 'The flat-topped houses and their peachy, sandy colour—they're so—un-European somehow. I suppose it must be the influence of the Turks. I mean . . .'

She was babbling hopelessly now, unable to stop herself because, with his fork lowered to his plate, he was simply watching her coolly, his expression alert and intent as if he were just waiting for her to run out of steam—and what would he do or say then?

'You could almost imagine that this scenery could be used as the backdrop to some biblical epic . . .'

Once more her hand gestured towards the view from the café, perched high up on the ramparts of the old city, but her eyes didn't follow the movement, and neither, she saw to her consternation, did Mark's.

'Instead they used the island to film *Popeye*.'

His smile barely existed; it was just the faintest curl at the corners of his mouth, but then, just when she thought he was not going to, he followed her lead.

'I know what you mean. I remember the first time I ever came here and saw that view. I was just nineteen and when I came up on to this part of the bastion I couldn't believe my eyes. That was when I lost my heart to Malta. I wanted to abandon my studies, leave everything, and come and live here—I even suggested the idea to my father.'

A wry note in his voice told Susannah just how his parent had reacted to that.

'Not a popular move?'

Mark shook his head emphatically, the movement making the sun catch on the glints of gold in his hair, striking sparks off them.

'He hit the roof—threatened to cut off my allowance.' His tone revealed how little that had concerned him, as his next words confirmed. 'To him, that was the ultimate punishment.'

But not to Mark, Susannah reflected privately. He would simply regard such a reaction as a challenge, and set himself to overcome it. To him, money was something to use. She recalled how, the previous year, she had been so astonished to learn that he was such a rich man because he didn't behave like one. His wealth was not used for flash or show, so much so that at first she had been totally unaware that it existed.

'You and your father are obviously not very much alike.'

Once more Mark shook his head, his mouth twisting slightly. 'Exact opposites. For him, everything has to be just so—disciplined—controlled——' The golden eyes slid to her face, a gleam of amusement lighting in them. '*He* was the bank manager.'

Susannah's smile mirrored his, recalling her interpretation of his job when they had first met. Now, she couldn't believe she had ever thought it possible that Mark would fit the description of bank manager. He was too much of an independent spirit, too forceful, to be confined in such a routine occupation.

'So that's where you get your financial wizardry from.'

'The knowledge, perhaps.' Mark sounded different, the relaxed amusement of a few moments earlier overlaid with a harder, clipped intonation. 'But the wizardry, as you call it—no. There's no magic in it, you know. It's just a calculated risk.'

'Mixed with a strong measure of inspiration,' Susannah put in. 'And your father——'

'Is definitely not into taking risks,' Mark finished for her. 'He's an eminently respectable but deeply conservative banker—the last in a long line of such characters.'

So how had Mark come by the gambler's instinct that had led to some of his more inspired investments? He might emphasise the calculation in what he did, but others would highlight the strong risk element instead.

Seeing Mark's grin, Susannah was thoroughly disconcerted to realise that she had spoken her thoughts aloud.

'Ah, well, that's a legacy from the black sheep of the family—on the other side—my maternal grandfather.'

He laughed suddenly, the sound warm as the sunny air, laced with an affection that had shaded his words; an affection which, Susannah now realised, had been missing when he had spoken of his father.

'That was something that my father couldn't plan for, as he did everything else in his life. My mother was just what he wanted—beautiful, stylish, cultured—but her father was all that he most abhorred. Gramps was an inveterate gambler with an appalling facility for backing losers, and he could never keep any money, even if he won—he always had one last "certainty"—which meant, of course that, inevitably, he lost the lot.'

She had never seen Mark like this before, Susannah reflected, privately acknowledging the way the smile that still lingered softened the firm line of his lips, giving them a warm, sensual appeal.

'Is he still alive?' she asked, intrigued by this insight into another, very different side of his life.

Still smiling, Mark nodded again. 'Very much so, and, even at eighty-three, still handing over most of his pension to the bookmakers. We have a trip to Ascot every year to celebrate his birthday—and for a week I finance his betting.'

Susannah felt as if the warmth of Mark's voice, his smile, was curling around her heart, lifting it in a new and unexpected way. She was seeing him in a very different light, one that illuminated an open and generous side to his nature. Clearly he cared about his grandfather very much.

'I take it your father doesn't go along.'

The glance Mark shot her was full of a shared understanding that made her heart jerk in instinctive response.

'He'd hate it. The way he and Gramps live their lives are at opposite ends of the spectrum. Financially at least, they don't even speak the same language.'

'So you're a mixture of both of them.'

'That's right, though Pa doesn't see it that way. He thinks I've been totally corrupted by Gramps' irresponsibility. He prophesied doom and destruction when I said I was leaving mainstream banking and setting up a consultancy—he was convinced I'd be bankrupt before the end of the year.'

'But surely now you've proved him wrong.' Susannah felt she was beginning to understand the hard edge that came into Mark's voice when he spoke about his father. Clearly, they shared none of the easy warmth that was so much a part of his relationship with his grandfather. 'He must have admitted that he was wrong.'

'My father never admits to mistakes. Sorry is not a word that appears frequently in his vocabulary.'

Nor in his son's, Susannah reflected with a twist of bitterness. But then she was dreaming if she thought that any idea of apologising for the way he had behaved last year had even entered his mind. She had come so close to really liking this Mark that she had forgotten about the other one, the one who, like the wolf Theo had described him as, had seen what he wanted in her and had cold-bloodedly set out to seduce her.

'We never really got to know each other last time, did we?' Mark's voice intruded into her thoughts, confounding her with the realisation that he, too, had been thinking of their previous visit to Malta.

'N-no, we didn't,' was all she could manage, her thoughts centreing once more on that first meeting.

She would have done so much better if she could have held on to that sense of fear that had gripped her in the beginning, the instinctive knowledge that this man was like some searing, incandescent flame, one that drew her like a moth to its light, but which, inevitably could only bring terrible pain and destruction when the lust that flared between them—because honesty made her admit that primitive, physical lust was at the bottom of it all—burned itself out.

It had been in an attempt to escape that instinctive rush of heated awareness that she had flung herself into the swimming pool on that first day, needing desperately to cool the feverish temperature of her body, the boiling pulse of hot blood in her veins. She had plunged in without a thought of how cold the water would be, coming up gasping for air before throwing herself into

violent physical action, swimming up and down as if in
an attempt to escape from some terrible demon that was
pursuing her. It was only when fatigue finally forced her
to a halt, breathing heavily and wiping the water from
her eyes, that Mark had moved, getting to his feet and
discarding the shorts which he wore over sleek black
trunks before sliding sinuously into the pool at her side.

'And what was all that in aid of?' he enquired, his
smoothly drawling tone raising the small hairs on the
back of her neck in shivering awareness.

With a furious movement she dashed her soaking black
hair back from her face, shaking her head violently so
that cold drops of water spattered all over the bronzed
muscles of his torso as he trod water easily beside her.

'Nothing at all!' she flung at him, her unthinking outburst combining with her earlier unwary movement to
create a wave that splashed into her face, making her
lose her grip on the side for a moment and splutter inel-
egantly as she struggled to regain her balance.

'Steady. . .'

Strong hands caught her before she could sink below
the surface, his grip on her arms firm and sure, sparking
off a chain of reaction that was like a series of tiny ex-
plosions all over her skin, making her toes curl under
cover of the water and her breath catch in her throat.
Suddenly it was all too much for her—the heat, the glare
of the sun on the sparkling water, the physical surge of
awareness that flooded through her. She had never felt
so aware, so out of control, and it frightened her. Simon
had never made her feel like this; with him she had felt
warm and safe and comfortable. But her brain wouldn't
focus on Simon. There was only this man, and he was
too big, too strong, too forcefully *male*—too close—
too. . .

'Let go of me!' Her voice was high and sharp. 'I don't
want this! I don't want anything from you! I. . .'

The words died in her throat as she saw his slow smile,
like that of a lazily confident tiger, a hunter who knew
that all it had to do was to reach out an indolent paw
and flatten its prey to the ground.

'I suggest, my dear Miss Adams, that you wait until
you're asked for—or offered—anything, before you start
refusing whatever it is you've decided I'm after.'

Then, as Susannah was still gasping both at the effects
of the water and his words, he moved his hands, sliding
them underneath her arms until they were resting on the
sides of her ribcage, those powerful fingers curling on
to her back, their warmth burning into the soft flesh
exposed by her low-cut turquoise swimming costume,
his broad palms disturbingly, dangerously close to the
swell at the sides of her breasts.

'I—I'm sorry.' She stumbled over the words, her heart
beating too fast, the blood rushing through her veins too
swiftly to be able to think straight. 'I—seem to have...'

'To have misread the signals?' he finished for her when
she couldn't complete the sentence. 'Perhaps.'

The tiger's smile widened, grew into a triumphant grin.

'But I, on the other hand, can read the message loud
and clear.'

Susannah felt as if the sun were affecting her brain,
making it whirl crazily so that she had to close her eyes
against the sensation of dizziness. Was she going completely out of her head, seeing things where there was
nothing? Feeling...?

But then she looked into those glowing golden eyes,
seeing, behind the mockery, the taunting gleam, a deep,
burning awareness that matched the way she felt deep
inside. She hadn't been imagining things, she told herself.
He wanted *something*—it was written all over his face—
stamped into every strong line of his body.

Or was she simply projecting her own feelings on to
him? Was his face like a mirror, throwing her own
awareness, her own sensitivity to everything about him
back at her? Susannah cursed the hot, betraying colour
that washed over her skin, making her wriggle uncomfortably in his painful grasp, wanting to free herself,
only to freeze in horrified consternation as her unthinking twisting movements caused his hands to move
over her body, his right palm coming to rest exactly over
the curve of her right breast.

Through the buzzing in her head she heard his swiftly
indrawn breath, the sound seeming to echo her own

choking attempt at protest, and his head went back
slightly, honey-coloured eyes burning into her dark blue
ones, seeing how shock and uncontrollable response gave
them a shadowed, bruised look.

'And what you are saying to me is——'

His grip on her tightened, drawing her irresistibly
closer, and even as Susannah's body stiffened in instinctive rejection she knew that her outward actions did
not mirror the way she was feeling internally. Deep inside,
at some unconscious and purely primitive level, every
nerve, every sense was coming sharply awake, opening,
responding to the physical essence of this man.

'Kiss me.'

He said it so softly that for a few seconds it didn't
register, and then, even as, blindly, she turned her face
to his, she realised it was not an instruction but his interpretation of what he believed her 'signals' meant.
Immediately she reeled back, eyes blazing.

'I am not——' she began, but he didn't let her finish.

'Kiss me,' he said again, this time with a very different intonation, one that deepened his voice, making
it sear over her sensitised nerves, setting light to a slow-
burning fuse deep inside her. *This* was an order and as
he issued it his head bent, his mouth taking possession
of hers.

This time there was no feeling of restraint, Susannah's
aroused body breaking free of the constraints she had
tried to impose on it earlier. She swayed towards him,
like a flower moving towards the sun, her lips opening
to his, and as his kiss took possession of her it was as
if their surroundings, the pool, the tables and chairs, the
whisper of the breeze ruffling the parasols, all faded into
a hazy blur. The sun was hot on her back, and soft waves
stirred by her movement lapped gently at her skin, their
caress only another gentle sensation to add to the effect
of so many more. Her body became limp, overcome by
a languorous delight, and a sensual dreaminess made
her sigh her response against his hard mouth, letting her
dark head drop back against his supporting arm.

It was as if she had never been kissed before in the
whole of her life; as if this was what she had been born
for, what her body had been yearning for from the

second in which she had entered the world, but only now had she become aware of what she needed. The flame that licked along the fuse inside her had burned it away completely, reaching the keg of gunpowder that was her unwoken sensuality, and blasting it open with such devastating ferocity that she thought the top of her head might blow off in the resulting explosion. Her legs seemed too weak to support her and she had to cling to Mark's powerful shoulders, feeling his grip on her tighten and knowing that without his strength to support her she would not be able to keep her head above water any longer.

It was only when she felt the cold splash of water on her face that she realised that they had moved far from the side of the pool and into much deeper water where even Mark, with the advantage of his superior height, could not keep his feet on the ground. As it came home to her that, emotionally too, that was the way things were, that she was drifting into deep water, without any idea of whether she would sink or swim, she wrenched her mouth from Mark's with a gasping cry. But he would not let her go; instead he caught her around the waist and swam with her to the edge of the pool, lifting her up on to the tiled surround before hoisting himself up beside her.

He was breathing as heavily as she was, Susannah realised dazedly, his chest heaving as if he had just swum for miles, each indrawn breath ragged and uneven, and she could feel her heart thud in the same difficult pattern, the damp material of her costume clinging to breasts that rose and fell rapidly as she tried to regain her composure.

'Who the hell are you?' Mark had regained enough control to speak, but his voice was still roughened and harsh, his words sounding husky as if forced from a painful throat.

Susannah knew that his question could not just be answered by giving her name, which, of course, he already knew from Andrea. It went much deeper than that, questioning in the most elemental way the fate and the primitive force of the attraction that had brought them together in that searing kiss.

'I don't know...' she managed, and in that moment she spoke the absolute truth because she didn't know or understand herself in the slightest.

Just a few months before, she had thought that she had her future all mapped out. She had her job, her flat, her family and friends—and she had Simon. It was all so thoroughly sensible, so logical, the exact opposite of Andrea's whirlwind romance and declaration of a total change of her lifestyle. It was what everyone expected from Susannah, the level-headed one of the two Adams daughters.

But then she had realised that she couldn't marry Simon, and from that moment on it seemed as if every part of her life had been turned on its head. She no longer knew who or what she was or what she wanted from her future. The one thing she would have said with any degree of confidence was that the last thing she needed was another man in her life, but that was before Mark Kingston had exploded into her life, and even on such brief acquaintance she knew that Mark could never be described as just another man.

'What's happening?' she asked shakily, her mental confusion showing in her voice.

'I don't know.' Mark shook his head, looking almost as dazed as she felt. 'Destiny? Fate? Call it what the hell you like, I just know I wasn't looking for anything like this. I was quite happy with my life the way it was—but *this* has hit me like a bolt from the blue.'

'A nuclear bolt...' Susannah added weakly.

She had never felt this way before; had never been so aware of any man's body before, the sound of his breathing, now slowing to something approaching normal again, the hypnotic hold of those bronze eyes, the sheer sensual impact of his tanned skin, still with water glistening on it. As she watched, a single, sparkling drop slid down from one muscled shoulder, trailing across the hard lines of his chest, through the slightly curling, darkened hair, and she found it impossible to resist the temptation to trace its path with one soft fingertip, feeling his immediate response, his swiftly indrawn breath, the clenching of his muscles in an uncontrolled, convulsive movement.

'Do you know what you're doing?' he demanded, his voice harsh and uneven once more. 'What it does to me to feel you touch me like that?'

The rough question stilled Susannah's wandering hand and for a moment she froze into immobility, her pink-varnished fingertip still resting on the warm satin of his skin, her gaze transfixed on that tiny point of connection between them, watching as it rose and fell with his breathing. She felt as if she had pushed her hand into a live electric socket, and the resulting current seared through her body, setting off a sensation like the sort of painful pins and needles which resulted from waking after a time of numbness. Every inch of her skin seemed to tingle and burn with reaction, her breasts becoming taut and achingly sensitive, their hardened nipples pushing against the turquoise fabric stretched across them. She found it difficult to breathe properly, her heart seeming to pound high up in her throat, making her light-headed and dizzy so that she let her lids fall closed against the whirling sensation.

'*Do you*?' Mark demanded more sharply, the urgency of his tone bringing her eyes flying open again to meet his burning gaze, his eyes like molten bronze, their pupils huge and dark so that she almost felt she could be drawn deep into them. Nervously she wetted painfully dry lips with her tongue, struggling to find the voice with which to answer him.

'I know,' she croaked, the weakness in her voice betraying the effort she was making to force the words past the tight knot that seemed to have formed in her throat. 'I know.'

Oh, yes, she knew how he was feeling; she could read the details of his response in his face and every faint movement of the long body beside her. She could read them, and recognise them because they exactly matched her own.

Unable to bear the hot intensity of his gaze any longer, she dropped her eyes to hide her confusion, and immediately wished she hadn't as she saw how the dark material of his swimming trunks clung lovingly, emphasising rather than concealing the physical evidence of his arousal. Immediately her heart leapt into a frantic, pounding beat that made her head reel, as much from reaction to her own thoughts as any part of Mark's behaviour.

Disturbingly, almost shockingly, Susannah found that the discovery of his physical response to her, far from embarrassing her, simply aggravated the way she felt. The rush of sensation shooting through her veins, the sense of need uncoiling in the lower part of her body, a need so sharp it was a devastating mixture of pleasure and pain, drove away all sense of shyness or constraint so that she lifted her head and looked him straight in the face once more, her eyes so dark that they were almost black.

'I *know*,' she said again, and this time it was a declaration of intent and of acceptance of what she now knew to be inevitable. 'I know just what's happening to you, because I'm feeling exactly the same thing.'

'Susannah? *Susannah*! Did you hear a word I said?'

As Mark's voice broke into her thoughts, Susannah started nervously and tried to force herself to think straight, not knowing, in her confusion, whether she had heard him in the past or the present day.

'Susannah, where have you gone to? Hey—come back to me!'

Vaguely she became aware of his hand moving in front of her face so that she blinked hard, her head jerking back.

'Hey——' his voice softened in concern, as his hand moved to rest lightly on her shoulder '—I'm sorry—I didn't mean——'

'Don't touch me!'

Still struggling to collect her scattered thoughts, her body still highly sensitised by the erotic pattern of her memories, Susannah found his touch, light as it was, totally unbearable. It was as if his fingertips were white hot, burning into her through the soft yellow material of her T-shirt, searing the delicate flesh like a branding iron, so that she flinched away with a jerky movement of rejection.

'Don't touch me! I can't bear it!'

His hand was snatched away as if he too felt the scorch of heat that had so distressed her, and it was only as her blurred vision cleared and she actually focused on his face, seeing it change swiftly, that she realised with a pang of regret that his expression had originally been one of concern, almost of gentleness, and by her reaction she had driven it away. Now it had been replaced by a look of cold indifference, one that made his face as hard as stone, his eyes just golden chips of ice above cheekbones over which anger and hostility had drawn his skin so tight that it was almost translucent.

I'm sorry—I didn't mean it, she wanted to say but hastily bit back the words, knowing them to be too dangerous. She couldn't let her attitude towards him soften in the least; it was far too risky—and she should know—she'd been there once before. She'd fallen into a trap based purely on feeling, not thinking straight, and was still struggling with the repercussions.

'As I said, a liar and a coward,' Mark murmured, the sardonic silkiness of his tone threaded through with a dark strand of danger, a note of warning that Susannah knew she would be wise to heed.

But the memories that had gripped her had been so vivid, setting her body as well as her mind aflame with remembered passion so that even now she ached physically in reaction, unable to think straight.

'I am not a coward,' she declared, lifting her head to glare at him, and immediately acknowledging her reaction to be a mistake as she flinched away from meeting that icy gaze, the searing contempt burning like acid, seeming to strip her skin away from her newly sensitised nerves.

'No?'

She wouldn't have believed that anyone could inject such dark scepticism into a single syllable. Mark seemed to have recovered his composure, his very calmness somehow more shocking than his blazing anger of only moments before, destroying what little was left of her self-control.

'Damn you—no!'

His smile was hateful, just a small, dangerous curl of his lips, sending a shiver down Susannah's spine in spite of the heat of the day.

'Forgive me if I don't believe you.' His tone made a cynical lie of his request for forgiveness and Susannah had to clench her teeth tightly together in order not to spit her fury into his face. 'But I can't doubt the evidence of my own eyes, and I see——'

'Only what you want to see!' Susannah broke in on him. 'Can't you get it through your thick skull that I feel *nothing* for you, not even the...?' She faltered nervously, hot colour flooding her cheeks as she hunted for the right word.

'The passion? Desire?' Mark inserted smoothly, his eyes dangerously hard, the lean body ominously still.

'The *carnality*—pure animal lust—that you awoke in me before.'

Susannah flung the words into his unmoving, impassive face, heedless of the possible consequences. So distraught herself, she needed to see him make some response—any response—show some sort of reaction instead of this unnatural, inhuman stillness.

'You can put it down to the effects of the heat—the wine—a passing fancy—an itch that had to be scratched—whatever—but it was never anything more, and now it's gone—finished! It's burned itself out.'

Had she finally got through to him? she wondered as she paused for breath. If only he would react in some way; his immobility was somehow more frightening than any anger she had ever seen.

'I want you to understand——' she began again, then stopped abruptly as he shook his head, his expression totally ruthless.

'What you *think* you want and what you actually do are two very separate things,' he said hardly. 'You're not thinking straight, my beautiful siren.'

'I'm thinking *perfectly* straight!' Susannah protested, not allowing her mind to let that 'beautiful' register, knowing it would throw her even further off balance if she admitted to even the faint flicker of pleasure the offhand compliment gave her. 'It's you who can't get the message. I...'

She took a deep, uneven breath and then brought the words out in a rush.

'*I don't want you*—in any way whatsoever.'

'Because I bore you?' The lightness of Mark's tone was dangerously deceptive; cold flames of anger burned at the back of his golden eyes, held ruthlessly in check for the moment only. She had really stung his pride with that remark, Susannah reflected on a quiver of apprehension.

It would be so much easier to say yes, he had bored her out of her skull; perhaps then he would leave her alone, the insult working where all else had failed. But even as she drew herself up to fling the defiant response at him, an inconvenient twinge of conscience forced her to admit that she could not be so dishonest. To do so would be to deny the genuine pleasure his company had brought her, as it had this afternoon, when he had given her such a fascinating insight into Malta's history.

And, no matter what she claimed, a further prick of scrupulous honesty forced her to admit, *boredom* was the last thing she had ever felt when she was with this man.

From the first she had found his company exciting and stimulating—and not just in the physical sense. After their explosive first meeting, he had pulled himself up short, imposing some degree of control on things.

'Believe me, I don't usually behave like this,' he had said, his voice shaken and rough. 'I don't usually come on so hard—or so fast. It's just I've never met anyone like you—look, let's start again, try and get things under control, at least for a while. Have dinner with me tonight.'

And of course she had agreed. It was when she was in her room, preparing for the evening ahead of her, that she first became aware of how her mood had changed, experiencing a sense of anticipation that was such a contrast to the tension that had gripped her for so long, tightening every muscle until it ached. The feeling of release had an effect like that of some sparkling wine, lifting her spirits so that she could throw off the burden of unhappiness that she had carried with her for so long.

Mark had made her laugh, he had been flatteringly attentive, with an ability to draw her out so that she had talked almost non-stop, about her family, her job, her newly acquired, half-decorated first flat—but not about Simon. That subject was still too painfully close to the surface of her mind, the wounds Simon had inflicted not yet properly healed, and, besides, the last thing she wanted to do was to destroy the new lightness of her mood with any recollection of the distress of the past.

As a result, when, as they lingered over a second bottle of wine, the stars growing bright in the darkening sky, Mark had asked quietly, 'And is there a man in your life?' she had shaken her head, switching on what she hoped was a convincingly bright smile.

'Not now...' Her voice deserted her and she covered the fact with an airy wave of her hand.

'What went wrong? He wasn't into commitment?'

'*He* was.' In spite of herself, Susannah couldn't suppress the shiver of reaction that shook her at the thought of the excessive demands for commitment that Simon had made.

'But it was not for you?'

'Definitely not—just the thought scares the hell out of me.'

She didn't want to be trapped like that again; all she wanted was for this wonderful, light-hearted mood, this exhilarating sense of freedom, to continue. Seeing Mark's eyes fixed on her face, she gave a slightly nervous laugh.

'Why are you looking at me like that?'

'Like what?'

'As if I'm the next item on the menu.'

Just for a moment Mark looked disconcerted, and she was stunned to see that a touch of colour washed across the high cheekbones, giving him a surprisingly vulnerable look.

'I'm sorry—no, I'm not,' he amended hastily, adding with a caressing softness, 'Would that be so terrible?'

'N-no.' She wasn't even fooling herself with her hesitation. The only thing that would be terrible would be for this wonderful evening to end, this special feeling to vanish. Her whole body—and her mind—were alive in

a way that she hadn't experienced for a long, long time—
in fact, she didn't think she had ever felt this way
before . . .

'I never meant that,' she muttered grudgingly, coming
back to the present reluctantly, knowing how dangerous
the admission was, the triumph he would feel hearing
it, but unable to lie.

'I know,' Mark disconcerted her by saying. 'So for
some reason you were angry enough to say the opposite
of what you really felt——'

'I wasn't thinking straight,' Susannah said hastily,
thoroughly disconcerted by how close he had come to
Andrea's comment in almost exactly the same situation.
The thought of his seeing through her so easily was distinctly worrying.

'But you don't find me boring,' Mark drawled, with
another of those worrying smiles, leaning back in his
chair with a deceptive display of nonchalance.

'N-no.'

In an effort to conceal the confusion she felt, Susannah
reached for her teacup, meaning to take a sip from her
drink. But just as she lifted it to her mouth, Mark disconcerted her totally by adding softly, 'Physically at
least.'

The cup crashed down into the saucer again.

'I never said——!'

'You didn't have to, my Calypso. Some things don't
need to be put into words—it's all quite clear to me
without that. I can read it in your eyes—in your
face——' his voice slowed, deepened '—it's written all
over your body——'

The golden eyes moved from her flushed and indignant face and slid slowly downwards over her slim
form in the most arrogantly insolent survey to which she
had ever been subjected, the obvious deliberate provocation depriving Susannah of the ability to speak, even
though she opened her mouth with the intention of firing
a scathing denial of his declaration at him.

But each time the necessary words failed her. Because
the trouble was that, even in the privacy of her own
thoughts, she couldn't deny what he was saying. Even

as he spoke, it was as if that hateful scrutiny had been an actual physical caress, bringing her whole body alive under its touch, her nerves tingling, her breasts aching, the blood rushing to the surface, washing her skin with betraying colour.

'Your tongue says one thing,' Mark went on, that smile deepening as he saw her attempts to speak, 'but your lovely body isn't quite so carefully guarded.'

Suddenly he moved, leaning forward again, his arms on the table, bronze eyes burning into her shadowed blue ones.

'Why deny it, Susannah? It was good for us last time; it could be so again. If you'll only loosen up, let yourself go——'

'Loosen up?' Susannah broke in, her voice unnaturally shrill. '*Loosen up*! I did that last time—I let myself go...'

Despairingly she shook her head, sending her black hair flying.

'I *let myself go* all right—but in the sense of lowering my standards. I *let go* so much that now my skin crawls with embarrassment when I think of it. But never again—do you hear? Never, ever again!'

CHAPTER SEVEN

SUSANNAH didn't quite know what she expected when she ended her outburst—anger possibly, or biting satire, certainly some sort of immediate response. Instead, Mark simply leaned back in his chair, arms folded across his broad chest, his eyes narrowed as he studied her face as coldly and analytically as if she were some specimen under a microscope, deliberately drawing out the silence until it was more than she could bear.

'And that,' she declared, her voice breathless and uneven, 'is quite definitely not one of the occasions on which I've said the opposite of what I really think. I meant every word. And now, if you don't mind, I'd like to go home.'

'Of course.'

Mark moved and spoke at last, stunning her by his calm response. But this time there was something very different about it, a constraint that spoke of rigid control imposed with ruthless determination, one that made shivers of apprehension run down her spine at the thought of what was yet to come. Because he wasn't going to leave it at that, she was sure of it.

'Whatever you say, Calypso—after all, Andi and Theo will be expecting us and we wouldn't want to worry them—would we?'

The sudden hardening of his voice on the question, the cold light in his eyes, left Susannah in no doubt that he meant the double-edged comment to strike home—which it did, twisting the nerves in her stomach painfully with the realisation that, in her anger, she had completely forgotten about her sister's problems, the price Mark was asking for his signature on the rescue deal for the hotels.

He had got to his feet, holding out his hand to help her up, looking every inch the perfect, courteous escort, she thought bitterly, just as he had done last year. At least this time she knew the two-faced act for what it was—a callous, manipulative, power game of the sort that he enjoyed in his working life—only this time he was playing with people's lives and feelings, their hopes and dreams, as well as their money. Deliberately ignoring that outstretched hand, she pushed back her chair sharply and stood up, blue eyes flashing defiance.

'Just what is it you want from me?' she demanded.

'Want?' Mark turned those golden eyes on her with an infuriating assumption of innocence, incensing her further.

'You know what I mean! Theo and Andrea—that contract—you *know* how important it is.'

He didn't help her, showing no sign that he understood what she meant, letting her stumble awkwardly over her words.

'Are you really going to force me——?'

'Force? My dear Calypso, I've never forced a woman yet. I don't intend to start with you.'

It should have been reassuring, so why did she not feel any such emotion, experiencing instead another painful twist of nervous apprehension?

'So——'

'So the situation is quite simple.' How she hated that carefully reasonable voice, knowing that it concealed the working of a calculating, ruthless mind. 'I'm here for a week—I want to see all the hotels, finalise the details with Theo. At the end of that time—if I'm happy—I'll sign the contract.'

He certainly made it sound straightforward, Susannah reflected privately, but the implications behind that subtly emphasised 'If I'm happy' made her blood run cold in her veins.

'Would it be too much to ask you to keep me company for that short time?'

Susannah had to admit that there was a sort of twisted logic in his request. Last year, he had anticipated a fortnight-long holiday affair—she refused to call it a romance—with her. By leaving as she had, she had deprived him of the second week, and now he wanted what he thought was due to him.

'Well?'

She weighed the idea in her mind. A week, he had said, and already one day was almost over. Six days were such a short time when balanced against the whole of Andi and Theo's—and of course baby Jamie's—future. Her thoughts went back to the earlier part of the day; that time had been like that first dinner, easy, relaxed—even enjoyable. That, she could cope with, but with Mark Kingston it couldn't be that simple.

'Keep you company,' she echoed faintly. 'And the rest?'

Mark's smile was slow, worryingly disarming, and he lifted his broad shoulders in a dismissive shrug.

'As you said, I'm a gambler. I'll leave it to chance.'

Susannah couldn't believe what she was hearing.

'But you must know that the odds are stacked against you.'

'Oh, no, Calypso,' Mark shook his head, those golden eyes glinting dangerously. 'I may gamble, but, unlike my grandfather, I never waste my money. You see, I only ever bet on certainties—and with you, I reckon my stake is perfectly safe. You may have persuaded yourself that what there was between us has burned itself out, but I'm afraid that you haven't convinced me. The next six days should be the perfect opportunity to find out which one of us is right.'

'Why, you...' Susannah couldn't find words insulting enough to respond to him.

'I don't mind waiting,' Mark continued imperturbably. 'I reckon it'll be worth it. After all, anticipation can only sharpen the appetite, making the final pleasure all the greater as a result.'

To add to Susannah's confusion, he treated her to the sort of smile that in the past had made her go weak at the knees.

'*Now* we'll go home.'

He was turning as he spoke, heading for the stairs down to the main part of the café, leaving Susannah with no option but to follow him. She had to make a special effort not to stumble on the uneven flagstones, her mind a blur of anger and confusion in the middle of which one memory stood out with bitter clarity.

She recalled one warm, sultry night twelve months before, when she and Mark had lain together, the sweat of passion still sheening their skin, their bodies languorous in the aftermath of lovemaking. The only reason why they hadn't become lovers on that first night had been because Mark had been the one to hold back, she remembered with a sense of shame. She had been unable to do so, would have rushed straight into his bed if he had let her, the wild need too strong to be denied. As it was, the short wait had seemed like an eternity, their final coming together a volcanic explosion that blasted her out of her former way of life and into a new world of sensation where nothing existed but her body and Mark's and the devastating pleasure they could create between them. Each succeeding night had increased rather than lessened that physical need, creating a new, greater hunger in the same moment that it satisfied the present one.

It had been some time before either of them could breathe normally again, let alone move or speak, but in the end, as she lay with her eyes closed, she felt Mark lever himself up on to one elbow and knew, without having to lift her heavy lids, that he was looking down at her relaxed, satiated body.

'It can't go on like this,' he had murmured, his voice so low that she barely caught it, and somehow she knew that he was speaking to himself, not to her, believing her to be asleep. 'It can't last.'

Her eyes tight shut, some instinct warning her not to reveal that she was actually awake, she heard him give a low, slightly shaken laugh.

'And would I want it to?'

One hand softly touched the side of her cheek and it took all Susannah's self-control not to open her eyes and press a kiss on his long fingers. A moment later she was intensely grateful for the fact that she hadn't moved, a cold sense of unease creeping over her as she sensed rather than saw Mark shake his head.

'God, no!' Shockingly, the laughter had gone, replaced by an ominously cold conviction. 'That's not for me—not at all what I'm looking for. But what the hell—

this'll burn itself out soon. It has to—I can't keep this act up for long.'

That was the last thing she had heard because at that point genuine sleep had claimed her, and when she had woken Mark was already up and had gone out with Theo. She had never seen him again, had never been able to confront him with her disquiet about what she had heard, because only an hour later her father had telephoned with the dreadful news about Simon.

As a result of that call she had hurried back to England, believing, once she had begun thinking clearly again, that she had had a narrow escape. Mark's conviction that the passion between them would soon burn itself out had been right, things would inevitably have come to an end, and probably sooner rather than later. Fate had intervened, breaking the spell abruptly and well before she was ready for it, but with the painful discovery that, far from being so very special to Mark, she was in fact just an available, reasonably physically attractive female—one gullible enough to swallow the line he spun her—she was forced to admit that it was better this way, better that she hadn't hung on until the bitter end, until Mark grew tired of her and made that fact plain. At least she had been spared the careless rejection, the unfeeling goodbye, which must have been what he had planned for the end of her holiday or whenever he grew tired of keeping up the act which, not knowing he had been overheard, he had acknowledged his behaviour to be.

But now it seemed that the desire Mark had felt for her was still there, and that time and distance hadn't worn it away—in fact the opposite. She was convinced now that her abrupt departure had stung his pride, put her into what she was sure must be a rare category of something he couldn't have. That must give her a curiosity value at least. After all, she doubted if many women would leave Mark Kingston, with his looks and money—most likely it was the other way round. And if that was the case, then her adamant refusal to have anything to do with him had probably only stimulated his interest further. What was it he had said? That anticipation sharpened the appetite.

Susannah shivered as a sensation like the slither of drops of ice slid down her spine. She felt cornered, trapped. If she continued to refuse Mark, then his desire would grow to meet the challenge he thought she offered him, but the alternative...

And there was a further complication, one she feared far more than any threat from Mark, and that was her own response. As Mark had flung at her earlier, the truth was that she was not as indifferent to him as she tried to claim. The physical yearning that he had been able to awaken so easily last year was still so very close to the surface that it took all her strength to resist it. The blind, unthinking response that ignored all the warnings of common sense or logical thought was not dead as she had thought but only dormant, threatening to burst out again in full strength no matter how she tried to stop it.

But she had to stop it. Her self-respect had barely survived the experience of the previous year; she had only just begun to build it back up again. The intensity of physical pleasure that she had experienced in Mark's arms, in his bed, could not be denied—but the price she had had to pay for it was way too high.

'Well, what did you think of the Victoria?'

'It was a dump!'

Susannah spoke without thinking, Mark's question breaking into thoughts that were already preoccupied and disturbed so that she had neither the time nor the coherence of mind to consider whether her answer was wise or to try to form a more careful one. The truth was that she had just been brought hard up against the reality of the problem that faced Theo in his attempt to restore the family chain of hotels to anything close to the standards demanded by British tour operators.

'But a dump with potential, don't you think?' Mark surprised her by replying. 'The trouble is that Gozo isn't the sort of place people come looking for excitement or nightlife, so we need some other sort of attraction. That's why I wanted to know your ideas about it.'

'My ideas—but I know nothing about hotels...'

She frowned her confusion. When Mark had insisted on her accompanying him to Gozo, where he was due to inspect the one hotel Theo's family owned on Malta's sister island, she had assumed that he was keeping her to her agreement to spend time with him, not taking much notice of his remark that he had a particular reason for wanting her with him this time.

'But you're naturally intelligent, have plenty of knowledge of the leisure industry, and, last year at least, you were full of ideas for changing the way things were organised where you worked.'

Susannah knew that her consternation must show on her face as Mark drew the car in to the side of the road, parking close to the edge of an impressive headland below which the intense jewel-bright blue-green of the sea sparkled beautifully. Did he remember everything she'd ever said? She'd forgotten until now how she had talked to him about the leisure centre, unable to reveal how her problems with Simon were affecting her feelings for her work, and so expressing her frustration at various practical problems she had recently experienced.

'That was...' she began, but then drew in her breath sharply as inspiration struck. 'What you should be doing is exploiting the island's natural assets. There's so much scope here for outdoor sports—scuba diving, water-skiing, surfing. After all, the hotel's so close to one of the few real beaches they have. You could develop it as an activities centre—perhaps add a health farm for those who were not so energetic and...'

Becoming aware of the way Mark was watching her, bronze eyes fixed on her face, she suddenly realised that her voice had sharpened with enthusiasm, her hands gesturing towards the hotel on the shore below them, and, her heart jerking painfully, she stumbled to a halt, hot colour washing her cheeks.

'Just an idea...' she managed awkwardly.

'And exactly the sort of thing I was looking for. What other sorts of facilities would you think of providing?'

'Oh, let me think...'

A sudden idea occurred to her. If she could sell the plan for a health farm to Mark, then perhaps he would no longer hold back over signing the contract with Theo. If she could persuade him that his investment would turn the Victoria into a goldmine then she would be able to solve her sister and brother-in-law's problems—and her own—in one swift move.

'All the obvious ones like squash, tennis, golf— perhaps even hikes to some of those archaeological sites you told me about.'

They had visited one of those sites only that morning, on the way to the Victoria, and Susannah had been entranced by the spectacle of the ruined prehistoric temples built almost three thousand years before.

'And there must be someone who could provide horses—on these country roads, riding would be a wonderful way to see the island.'

Staring out at the distant horizon, no longer inhibited by his watchful eyes, she let her thoughts run wild, her imagination fed by the magic of the island itself, mixed with her own dreams of the sort of place she would have liked to work in. Mark listened in silence until at last she ran out of steam, ending on a small, slightly embarrassed laugh.

'So there you are—all you need now is someone to run the place.'

'I think I've found her.'

'What?' Susannah couldn't believe she had heard right. 'You . . . ?'

'You'd be perfect for the job—if you want it.'

'But . . .'

It was a struggle to disguise the flare of excitement in her eyes as she considered the prospect that he might actually mean what he'd said. It would be a wonderful challenge—the sort of thing she'd only ever dreamed of. She could get away from the leisure centre and all its bitter memories, work here, on this wonderful island——

'But you don't know if I can do it.'

Mark shrugged away her protests. 'I'm prepared to take the risk. Call it gambler's instinct if you like—but anyone can see that the idea excites you. You care about it, and such enthusiasm is invaluable. Besides, you told me yourself that you'd recently been promoted in your present job.'

'Oh!' Susannah had to bite down hard on her lower lip to hold back the cry of distress that almost escaped

her at the recollection of how she had come by that promotion, and she had to look away sharply, praying that
Mark would believe she had screwed up her eyes against
the glare of the sun and not to hide their betraying
brightness.

'You care about these islands too—I saw it in your
face at Mdina, and again at the temples this morning.'

'You're right,' Susannah murmured. 'Like you, I think
I'm falling in love with this place—it has a wonderful
character and such a fascinating history.'

'And because of that I know I could rely on you not
to damage that sense of the past even when creating
something for the future.'

Could she do it? Susannah let her eyes drift to the
dilapidated building of the Victoria Hotel below them.
It would be a challenge, a new beginning, a chance to
work with Andi and Theo——

And with Mark. Belated realism slashed through her
dream like a cold knife.

'Is this another condition of your investment?'

She knew the answer as soon as she had spoken and,
seeing the way his face changed, growing hard as stone,
immediately wished the impulsive words back.

'I told you what I wanted.' Mark's voice was clipped
and cold, and it was only after hearing it that Susannah
realised how relaxed and pleasant his mood had been
until then, the loss of the former ease of communication
striking home painfully.

'My company,' she snapped, hiding her distress behind
attack, giving the words a deliberately ambiguous intonation, hating the way she had been forced to remember just why she was here, the blackmail he had
used to get what he wanted.

'Your company,' Mark returned, a dark note in his
voice sending a shiver of apprehension down her spine
in spite of the sun. 'But think about the job.'

Susannah managed an inarticulate murmur that might
have been agreement as he swung the car back on to the
road, unable to speak properly because of a painful
tension in her throat. She could never take the job because it would mean working with Mark, and she knew
that she would never be able to face the inevitable ten-

sions that would bring. And yet earlier, when they were exploring the temples, as at Mdina, she had positively enjoyed being with him, falling under the spell of the ancient site—and Mark's company—so that the time they spent there had simply flown.

But then she seemed to be condemned to suffer these sorts of ups and downs wherever Mark was concerned, which was hardly surprising when you considered how things had been between them last year. They had become lovers before they had begun to know anything about each other, when most people usually did things the other way round.

Covertly she slid her eyes to the long, powerful form of the man beside her, her senses coming tinglingly alive as she acknowledged the magnetic pull of forceful masculinity, the bright gleam of his hair in the sunlight, the way his white jeans and black T-shirt clung to the strong lines of his body. She couldn't forget that she knew exactly what he looked like under the close-fitting clothes; the memory of the tightly muscled torso, the long, lean legs was as vivid in her mind as if she had seen them yesterday and not all those months ago. Whatever else she might think of him, he was a devastatingly sexually attractive individual, she admitted privately, a man to match all others up against. The trouble was she had a sneaking, uncomfortable suspicion that very few others would ever compare with him.

'Where are you going now?'

'What would you like to see?'

'Calypso's cave?'

She made the suggestion hesitantly. Since the visit to Mdina three days before, she had puzzled about the name Mark had called her, finally asking her sister about it and learning that, in ancient mythology, Calypso was supposed to have been the nymph who had cast a spell over Ulysses when he was shipwrecked on her island.

'The island is supposed to have been Gozo—and there's a cave there where Ulysses is supposed to have lived with her for seven years,' Andrea had told her.

Mark shot her a swift, narrow-eyed look and instinctively she nerved herself for some pointed comment, but surprisingly none came. 'There's nothing much to see,' was all he said. 'It's a singularly unimpressive and murky hole—but if that's what you want...'

'Well, you were right.' Susannah's disappointment showed in her voice as she surveyed the supposedly magical hole in the rocks. 'Calypso's cave is a real non-event. No one in their right mind—ancient hero or not—could have wanted to live there for seven years.'

'Ah, but then Ulysses had other things to distract him——'

The glance Mark slanted at her face was bright-eyed with the laughter that warmed his voice, and Susannah found herself responding to it with an ease that she would have considered impossible only the day before.

In fact, worries about this trip had kept her awake long into the night, a prey to all the vagaries of the emotional seesaw as she tried to convince herself that all would be well, that he had said that he wanted her company, nothing more. But a few moments later, with that ominous 'I only bet on certainties' sounding over and over inside her head, she knew that she had walked right into a tiger's lair, and that now she could find no way out. She could say she had changed her mind, of course, but if she did she was sure that Mark in turn would immediately refuse to sign the vital contract, and Andrea's bubbling gratitude for the way she had handled things so far, keeping Mark 'sweet' as she put it, had been more than enough to convince her that she had done the right thing in agreeing to his terms in the first place. The trouble was that Andi didn't understand just what keeping Mark sweet entailed.

Eventually she had fallen asleep, but not into the peaceful oblivion she had hoped for. Instead, her dreams had been haunted by images of a tall, strong body, gleaming bronze hair, and a wide, flashing smile. In her sleep she had lived again through every one of the sensual, passionate nights she and Mark had shared the previous year, the erotic intensity of her fantasies so heated that when she woke she found herself bathed in sweat, her heart still pounding in remembered response, and when she had joined Mark at the breakfast table she had found it impossible to meet his eyes for fear he would read the impact of her nocturnal imaginings in her own shadowed blue gaze.

But now she found herself relaxing, her unease evaporating like mist before the sun. When Mark was like this, there was no way she could fault his manner. If he was once more going to assume the role of easygoing, knowledgeable, friendly guide, then she was sure that she would be able to cope.

So now, as they moved away from Calypso's disappointing home, she easily managed a smile in response to Mark's teasing.

'Oh, come on!' she protested. 'He'd have to be something of a masochist to enjoy living there!'

'You obviously don't believe in romantic love, then,' Mark astounded her by commenting. 'You don't think a woman's charms could blind a man to everything else?'

Disturbingly, some of the laughter had been erased from his voice, but Susannah determined to act as if she hadn't noticed it.

'That isn't love, it's delusion.'

'Who taught you that?' Mark's voice was worryingly sharp.

'Experience.' Simon had declared that once he had met her he couldn't think of anyone else—and Mark himself had said much the same thing. But neither of them had really been thinking of her—only of themselves. Not giving him a chance to question her further, she rushed on, 'And, besides, Calypso wasn't an ordinary woman. She was a—what did you call it?—a nymph, an enchantress. She put a spell on Ulysses.'

'And isn't that what love is—a sort of enchantment?'

Mark was concentrating on steering the car along the narrow, potholed roads and didn't see the glance that Susannah shot him, unsettled by the sudden turn the conversation had taken.

'Love...' she echoed uncertainly, and then stopped abruptly, silenced by a painful memory, seeing once again Simon's face, hearing the break in his voice when he had declared, 'But Suzi, I *love* you! I always have and I always will! You're my world, my life. Without you...'

'What Calypso felt for Ulysses wasn't love, it was obsession.'

She rushed into hurried speech in order to distract herself from her bitter recollections, mixed in with which was the stunning realisation that she had barely spared Simon a thought since she had arrived on Malta. How could she have forgotten all that had happened? How had she let Mark Kingston drive all of it from her mind for a second time?

'She wanted him like a possession, and so she held on to him without a thought for his feelings——'

'Do you really think someone can be held like that if they don't actually want to?'

Something in Mark's tone, softly questioning as it appeared on the surface, made all the tiny hairs on the back of Susannah's neck lift in nervous apprehension.

Not you, she reflected inwardly. No one could ever tie you down, hold you if you wanted to be free. A sharp sense of bitterness stabbed at her as she recalled his relieved laughter when, believing her to be asleep, he had assured himself that their mutual passion would soon burn itself out, the cold certainty with which he declared that he wouldn't want it to last. No one would ever hold him as Simon had tried to hold her, trying to force her into the sort of relationship she couldn't cope with.

'But *was* Ulysses willing? Don't some versions say that he was held prisoner here? Either way, she's supposed to have used some sort of magic...'

Which brought them close to the uncomfortable subject of love once again, she realised, hastily changing tack.

'Didn't she promise him immortality or something?'

'If he'd marry her,' Mark nodded. 'But she was forgetting that he already had a wife——'

'Oh, yes, Penelope. I'd forgotten about her too.'

'Of course, there wasn't just Calypso. She bore Ulysses two sons.'

'Which must have complicated matters. After all, children need their fathers. Would you ever want children, Mark?'

Even as she spoke the words, she couldn't quite believe she was actually saying them. Mark's easy, relaxed attitude, her enjoyment of the beauties of Gozo, the warmth of the sun that shone down on them, all had combined to loosen her tongue until she had found herself speaking with a spontaneity that was perhaps not the wisest of moves.

For a couple of long, taut seconds she thought he wasn't going to answer her, and feared that her impulsive question had taken her over the invisible line which defined what was acceptable and what not. But then at last he lifted his broad shoulders in a faint shrug.

'With the right woman,' he said, the flatness of his tone implying that he had never yet met that perfect creature.

Susannah was astounded by the sharpness of the stab of pain that struck at her in response to his offhand reply. Surely she hadn't seen herself as a candidate for the position of mother of his children?

'And what about you?'

'Oh—I always said I wanted to have two of each.'

Her voice came and went in the most disturbing way because she was unable to concentrate her mind on controlling it properly, her wayward thoughts straying instead to the dangerously appealing image of the children Mark would father—beautiful, tall, strong, children, with his glowing tawny hair...

'And, of course, spending time with young James is enough to make anyone feel broody...'

No, that was a mistake; she knew it as soon as she saw the faint frown that drew his dark eyebrows together. But even as she acknowledged privately that what she was about to say was dangerous, that she risked ruining once and for all the relaxed atmosphere she had worked so hard to create, she also knew that she couldn't hold back.

'Doesn't it worry you to think of what you're doing to that family? Don't you have a conscience?'

'What am I doing?' Mark enquired, with a carefully assumed act of innocence that set her teeth on edge.

'You know! You're just playing with them—you hold their future in your hands and you don't care! You can make or break Theo——'

'You have a tendency to overdramatise,' Mark drawled sardonically. 'It would be purely a business decision.'

'Business!' Susannah didn't even bother to try to hide her disgust. 'It isn't business—it's a psychological power-game. You're the worst sort of bully—preying on people weaker than yourself, like a cat with a mouse in its claws. I——'

A terrible thought suddenly struck her. How far would he actually go? Was it all part of his callous manipulation of things—even the plans for the Victoria—the offer of a job? There was the bitter taste of acid in her mouth.

'I don't even know that you really are going to invest——'

'Oh, you can take that as definite,' Mark cut in smoothly. 'From the time of my first visit to Malta, I've always dreamed of owning property here.'

'Then Theo...' Was he saying that he intended to buy into the business, no matter what? In that case, where did that leave her—and his threats—if she didn't co-operate?

'Theo was the push I needed. Meeting him again reminded me of my dream.' Golden eyes flicked swiftly to Susannah's face and then back to the road. 'I'd got so bogged down in my life that I'd almost lost sight of it. That chance encounter put me back on the path to achieving it.'

So would he be prepared to abandon that long-held dream simply to spite her? A rush of hope flooded Susannah's mind, only to be crushed down again by Mark's next statement.

'If this particular plan doesn't work out there'll be something else.' Suddenly his voice changed, becoming deeper, huskier in a way that made all the tiny hairs on the back of her neck lift in apprehension. 'It's proving a little more complicated than I anticipated—but now I know what I want there's no going back. Like Ulysses, I'm completely bewitched.'

That 'Now I know what I want' sounded ominously inside Susannah's head, reminding her uncomfortably of Theo's comment that 'If Mark Kingston wants something, he gets it.'

A moment later Mark had performed another of those bewildering switches of mood that had kept her feeling as if she were on some emotional rollercoaster throughout the week.

'I think it's time we ate—you must be starving. How about a late lunch in Rabat? And after that, if you've got any energy left, you can explore the Citadel.'

'I'd like that.' Susannah spoke because some response was needed, but her thoughts were busy with the puzzle of her own reactions.

What was happening to her? Less than twenty-four hours before, she had anticipated this trip with a sense of dread, but somehow in the short time she had spent with Mark all those fears had disappeared—on a personal level at least—so much so that she couldn't believe she was the same person who had ever felt them.

She had meant to keep a watchful eye on events, being wary with Mark, not allowing him to affect her in any way. She knew that, given half a chance, he would turn her world upside-down just as he had twelve months before, and she had determined not to let that happen.

Or she had thought that she knew that. Now it seemed that, even though nothing had changed, and the threat to Theo and Andi still hung over her, she didn't know whether she was on her head or her heels. The sense of loss she had experienced in the moment when she had faced up to the possibility that everything Mark had done was solely designed for his own selfish ends had brought home to her the way that, in her supremely rational and sensible consideration of things, she had neglected one important fact—her own emotions. At the start of the day, those emotions had warned her that Mark was a man to be feared, a man to be kept at a safe distance, if she had any sense of self-preservation or self-esteem; but now it seemed that they were telling her the exact opposite. She wanted to spend more time with him; in fact she never wanted the day to end. It was as if, here on Calypso's island, the magic of the place had touched them too. Or was that, too, the sort of delusion that she had thought Ulysses' love to be? The trouble was that she didn't know which to believe; and the real problem was that if she couldn't trust her own feelings then what chance did she have of getting out of this with her pride—and her heart—intact?

CHAPTER EIGHT

'THAT was an amazing day! I really enjoyed myself.'

Susannah leaned against the rail on the top deck of the ferry boat and watched as Gozo slipped away from them, giving a faint sigh of regret at the thought that their visit was over.

'I'm glad about that.' Mark's voice was deep and relaxed. 'I always find Gozo a specially magical place.'

'It is, isn't it?' Susannah nodded slowly, her eyes on the horizon where the spires of the church that dominated Mgarr harbour could still be seen. 'It seems to belong to a totally different age. I mean, where else could people leave their keys in the lock when they're out so that visitors can let themselves in? I know you told me it was so, but I wouldn't have believed it if I hadn't seen it for myself.'

She gave another sigh, deeper this time.

'I'm sorry to be leaving...'

That brought a question into her mind, one that was decidedly unsettling to her mental equanimity. Was it only the island she was sorry to leave, or was there more to it than that? She couldn't help wondering whether the sense of loss she was feeling was because the day itself, rather than just the visit to Gozo, was almost over. It had seemed as if, on the peaceful island, all the hostility between herself and Mark had evaporated, their conflict suspended, and she had been content to let the new peace between them continue, reluctant to destroy the atmosphere by reviving any of the causes of dissension.

'You can always come back again.'

Yes, but could she recapture that special atmosphere again—or had that simply existed because they had been there together? Once more, Susannah pushed the disturbing thoughts from her mind. Call it cowardice, call it blind delusion, or perhaps just plain foolishness, but she didn't want to spoil what was left of the day with such worrying problems, particularly when she knew that the answers to her questions wouldn't be easy to find. With a last, longing glance at the island, which was now just a smudge on the horizon, she turned to Mark.

'You were going to tell me about the stone shelves we saw outside some of the houses—a folk tale, you said——'

'Oh, yes——' Mark grinned widely. 'They are supposed to have been a way of indicating that a woman inside the house was looking for a husband. When the daughter of the house got to be of marriageable age, her father would put a potted plant on the shelf by the door and it would stay there until a would-be suitor came along to take it down.'

'My Dad would have liked the sound of that!' Susannah laughed. 'He was desperate to marry Andi and me off—mainly because he wanted grandchildren so much.'

Her laughter faded, destroyed by a rush of memory. Neither of her parents had been able to understand why she had rejected Simon's proposal of marriage; they had both seen him as perfect son-in-law material. Perhaps that had been part of the problem, she reflected. He had been *too* perfect, too safe, quite without that streak of danger that set some men apart—Mark Kingston, for example. Contemplating the prospect of her parents having Mark as a son-in-law made her mind boggle, and she hastily refocused her thoughts on to more mundane matters.

'He wants a football team at least. He dotes on little James.' A rueful smile crossed her lips. 'Dad's very much the old-fashioned type. All he wanted for his daughters was that they should marry, settle down and provide him with a flock of grandchildren.'

Mark's soft laughter held a note of shared understanding that was unexpected.

'I know the feeling. I don't think my Pa will believe I've really grown up until I present him with the requisite heir to carry on the family line.'

'A daughter won't do?' Susannah teased, knowing the answer already.

'Please!' The look Mark turned on her was warm with amusement, twisting something sharply deep in the pit of her stomach. 'A female bank manager? That's his private nightmare.'

But Mark hadn't inherited any of his father's chauvinistic views, Susannah reflected. Several times during the afternoon he had returned to the subject of the plan for the dilapidated Victoria, discussing the matter with her with no constraints, treating her very much as an equal, wanting her comments and listening to them with a flattering appreciation.

'Worse than a female bookmaker?'

'That would make him cut his throat—but Gramps would love it.'

'He sounds a wonderful character. I'm afraid that, compared to him, my grandparents are very tame and conventional—though I only know my mother's parents. Dad's mother and father died when he was young—his father when he was only five. I think that's why he wants us to have a family so much.'

'And how do you feel?'

The question was put very casually, Mark's attention apparently fixed on the point where Comino, the third and smallest of the Maltese islands, had just come into view. But something about the stance of the strong body next to hers, a new tightness in every muscle, alerted Susannah to a change in his mood.

'Feel?' she questioned cautiously.

'About marriage. Does the idea appeal?'

'It did once. In fact, everyone was convinced I'd be married well before Andi.' Her laughter was hollow, slightly shaken. 'Things don't turn out quite as you expect them to.'

'What made you change your mind?'

Susannah winced inwardly, Mark's question coming too close to memories that were difficult to cope with.

'I just realised it wasn't for me,' she declared abruptly. 'Like you, I decided that a single life was much more fun.'

'When did I say that?'

As Mark straightened up from where he had been leaning against the ship's rail, Susannah had to blink hard, unable to believe the evidence of her own eyes. It was as if some sort of transformation had taken place right before her eyes, as if the Mark with whom she had spent the day had been spirited away and a total stranger put in his place. The easygoing, amusing, friendly companion of the trip to Gozo had vanished, and in his place was a cold-eyed, harsh-faced, arrogant devil whose handsome features had hardened until they looked as if they were carved from stone, his mouth compressing to a thin, hard line.

'*When*?' he demanded, so aggressively that instinctively Susannah took a couple of steps backwards, away from him. The top deck of the ferry was almost empty, most people having sought protection from the cool of the evening in the main cabin where there was a bar serving drinks and coffee, and she was suddenly painfully aware of the fact that she was in a very isolated position here, with this dangerous and powerful man who towered over her threateningly.

'Last year—you—I . . .'

She stumbled over the words, hunting desperately through her memories, realising now that he hadn't actually said the words to her face, only revealing his true thoughts in the things he had said when he had thought she was asleep. In her present situation she doubted the wisdom of revealing that she had in fact heard him.

'You said—you weren't looking for any sort of relationship—that it was the last thing you wanted——'

'And it was,' Mark cut in harshly. 'I liked my life the way it was; I enjoyed being free . . .'

And that was what had appealed to her about him, Susannah had to admit. After Simon, and the unbearable pressures he had put on her, she had been fearful of any intense feeling. She had needed a way to escape and Mark had seemed to be the perfect person to provide just that.

'*You* were the one who said that the idea of commitment scared the hell out of you.'

Because then commitment had meant the sort of demands Simon was making on her. It had seemed that he wanted to own her, possess her completely.

'And *you* made it plain that you felt the same——'

'Of course I did,' Mark snarled. 'I would have said anything to——'

'To get me into your bed!' Susannah finished for him when he hesitated.

Bitterness welled up inside her, bringing a sour taste to her mouth, when she saw how he didn't deny it, simply acknowledging her accusation with a brusque inclination of his head, the setting sun casting a fiery glow on his tawny hair.

'You weren't exactly reluctant on that score,' he stated quietly, but with a dangerous edge to his voice, one that made Susannah shiver as if an icy hand had just gripped her heart.

'I . . .'

Unable to refute what he had said, she could only stare at him, transfixed by the cold gleam in his eyes, their gold turned to molten bronze by the sunset, the way his skin was drawn so tightly over his high cheekbones that white marks were etched around his nose and mouth. Suddenly she was reminded of the portraits of the sixteenth-century Knights of St John, the early rulers of Malta, that she had seen in the Grand Master's palace in Valletta. They had stared out at the world with just that expression of arrogant self-confidence on their faces and, just for a moment, her imagination running away with her, she thought she could almost picture Mark in the Knight's black cloak with the white eight-pointed cross painted on it.

'You practically threw yourself into my arms,' Mark flung at her coldly. 'I just gave you what you wanted.'

'What we both wanted!' Susannah found her voice at last, though she winced at the high, rather desperate edge to it. 'You——'

A cynically questioning lift to one eyebrow, half hidden by the gathering shadows, silenced her as effectively as if he had slapped her hard across the face.

'You don't know what I wanted, Susannah. You didn't stay around to find out.'

'We had seven days——'

'*Seven days*,' he echoed, turning the words from a simple statement into a bitterly black irony. 'Even Calypso gave Ulysses seven years, but you——'

'You never said you wanted anything else!'

Desperation gripped Susannah, making her feel as if she was trapped in a corner, her back pushed firmly up against the wall. Seven days, he had said, and only she knew how she regretted every second of that time of madness, the time before she had come to her senses and realised that she had thrown herself into Mark's arms in an attempt to forget, as one might use alcohol or drugs, only becoming aware of just how foolish and self-destructive she was being when it was too late.

'I just assumed——'

'You *assumed*!'

Susannah shrank from the livid fury in Mark's tone as once more his repetition of her words turned them into something very different, something deadly to her peace of mind, terrifyingly dangerous.

Was he claiming that *he* had wanted more than that—more than the holiday-fling, no-ties, no-commitments affair that she had been so sure was all there was between them? He couldn't possibly mean that. After all, she had heard him herself: he had said that he was just waiting for things to burn themselves out. It was true that the phone call she had received had broken things up earlier than either of them had actually anticipated, but burn themselves out they inevitably would have done. The flames of passion which had flared so hotly between them had been incandescent but insubstantial, no roots to fasten them to the ground, nurture them for any length of time.

When it occurred to her that perhaps those flames had never died, that, in spite of everything, they still burned in her body, springing to life at the touch of Mark's hand, his kiss, she hastily flinched away from considering the possible implications of such a thought.

'You assumed,' Mark said again, his voice lowering to a threatening hiss. 'Did you ever *ask*?'

Susannah felt as if she had been struck a powerful blow in the chest, driving all the air from her body so that she gasped out loud. No, she admitted to herself, she hadn't asked; she hadn't *dared* to ask. She had come to Malta to escape from Simon, feeling that if she didn't get away she would break, shatter into tiny little pieces.

Mark had swept her off her feet. He had seemed to offer exactly what she needed—mindless, carefree pleasure, no strings, no pressures of any sort, either emotional or physical, and she had not stopped to question, to probe any deeper. To do so was to risk exposing the fears Simon's behaviour had created in her. It was only later that she had thought to question whether what she had felt she had needed then was in fact best for her.

'Don't tell me you were planning on proposing!'

Bitter cynicism hid the shake of fear in her voice. This was precisely why she hadn't wanted to probe any further. Just the thought of Simon's proposal and all that had followed it made her feel weak and desperately vulnerable, and it would all have been so much worse twelve months ago.

'No,' Mark said slowly. 'I can't say that.'

It was the answer she would have said she wanted; the one that freed her from any of the sort of pressure Simon had put her under; the one she had been convinced he would have given her if she had asked him such a question last year. Then she would have welcomed it gladly, so why did she now feel the sharp stab of disappointment, a strange emptiness in the pit of her stomach?

'Good,' she managed, wondering if it was only in her own ears that her response lacked any degree of conviction. 'That's fine, then . . .'

With ruthless determination she strengthened her voice, making it sound rather better, rather more confident.

'So we both know where we stand——'

'And that is?'

It was now too dark to see Mark's face clearly but his tone of voice was distinctly worrying, its sarcastic bite stinging sharply.

'Why—where we were when I first arrived,' she stammered. 'I—you—we had a holiday fling but now it's over——'

Once more she broke off abruptly, silenced by the slow, adamantly negative movement of his head, just a darker, more substantial shadow in the gathering dusk. It was thoroughly disconcerting trying to conduct a conver-

sation with someone whose features and expression were
obscured in this way. She wished she could see something that would give her more of a clue as to what he
was thinking.

But then Mark spoke again and, hearing his voice, she
felt suddenly that not seeing his face was in fact a great
relief.

'You're doing it again, Calypso,' he drawled sardonically. 'I—we——' he mocked her stumbling intonation, making Susannah wince inwardly at his black
cynicism. 'I told you before—what we had is not over.'

'But I...'

They were drawing near to the dock at Cirkewwa, and
below her, on the lower deck, she could hear the sound
of the bustle as the ferry's crew prepared for their ar-
rival, the noise of the boat's engines changing as they
began to manoeuvre into place.

'I don't want——'

'What *you* want doesn't count, my darling Calypso,'
Mark broke in once more, his words slicing into hers
like an ice-cold blade. 'I went along with that before,
but not again. This time it's my turn. We're not playing
by your rules any more, my lovely, but by *mine*.'

The threat implicit in his last words was ominously
emphasised by the heavy thudding of the boat against
the side of the dock, jolting Susannah forward so that
she would have fallen if Mark hadn't reached out to catch
her. Roughly he dragged her up against him, the hard
strength of his body crushing hers as he held her so tightly
that there was no chance of escape.

'And what I want is *this*,' he muttered thickly, his head
coming down swiftly, cruel lips capturing hers, bruising
them savagely.

In the darkness it was as if all Susannah's other senses
were heightened because she couldn't see. She could feel
the heat of his body pressed against hers, hear his
quickened breathing, scent the clean aroma of his skin
which smelled of the sun and the wild tang of sea spray.
This must be what it felt like to be blind, she thought,
her mind hazing under the sensual onslaught of his kiss,
her legs threatening to buckle underneath her, her whole
body suffused by a golden warmth.

Under cover of the concealing night, Mark's hands pushed roughly under her jacket, making her shudder in uncontrolled response as they explored the slender lines of her body, tracing paths of burning fire through the thin material of her T-shirt.

'Mark!'

In spite of her efforts to hold it back, his name was a muffled cry of delight against the brutal pressure of his mouth as she felt her whole body come alive in response to his urgent caresses, every inch of her suddenly taut with an aching need that soon centred as a hot ache between her thighs, her nipples yearningly hard and thrusting wantonly towards the heat of his hands.

His laughter was a harsh sound of triumph deep in his throat as he pushed her T-shirt up out of his way, the cool rush of air on her exposed skin making her gasp out loud, a gasp that turned into a cry of delight as, hidden in the black shadows of their private corner of the deck, he lowered his head and drew one delicate tip into the heat of his mouth, sending shuddering waves of pleasure through every inch of her aroused body.

'This is what I want!' he muttered thickly. 'This is how it should be! You can't let this die, Calypso—it's what we were put on earth for—to do this...'

Turning his attention to her other breast, he treated it to a second, heartbreakingly brief caress, one that made her heart kick wildly, a faint moan of distress escaping her at the brevity of her delight.

'And this...' Once more his burning mouth closed over her delicate flesh. 'You can't let things end—can't let them fade away so unsatisfactorily. You know this is what you want too.'

'But—not here...' Susannah panted, hardly able to form the words, the sound of the blood pounding through her veins drowning her own voice.

'Of course not. I may be crazy—but not completely off my head. Come to my room tonight, darling...' His voice was low, husky, weaving a spell as wild as any enchantment the nymph had ever cast over the ancient Greek hero. 'Calypso, come to me tonight—let it be the way it used to be...'

'Mark...'

Susannah swayed in his grasp, too weak to think straight.

'Mark . . .' she began again, not knowing what she was going to say.

'Yes?'

His voice was thick with desire and once more he lifted his head to look deep into her eyes, wide and dark in the moonlight. What he saw there made him laugh again, his cynical satisfaction searing through even the sensuous delirium that held her in its grip.

She had been a fool, she realised with a terrible sense of desperation, a naïve, trusting fool. Lulled into a false sense of security by the peaceful atmosphere of Gozo, she had allowed herself to believe that the face Mark had shown her throughout the long, delightful day had been his true one. She had actually come to believe that he had meant what he said when he had told her that all he wanted was her company, even begun to read into his words hints that he had no intention of carrying out his threat against her sister and her husband. Now reality had slapped her hard in the face with the realisation that it was all just another of his power games, a cynical manipulation of her feelings, simply a different way of getting what he wanted.

'No!'

Like some drowning person about to go down for the third time, she flung her head back, dragging in deep, raw breaths of air, the cold rush into her lungs driving away some of the heated delirium, so that from somewhere she found the strength to wrench herself away from him, even though her yearning body screamed a desperate protest at the move.

'No!'

Her voice was too weak, too shaken; it was carried away soundlessly on the breeze.

'I said no!' she tried again, more successfully this time. 'I've had enough——'

'Perhaps you have, my beautiful nymph.' Mark's response was laced with a silken menace that terrified her more than his earlier cold anger. 'But I haven't even started yet. The little you gave me last year was barely enough to awaken me to the delights of your lovely body.

By keeping your distance this time, you've simply sharpened my appetite. If I was hungry before, now I'm starving...'

His dark head swooped, snatching rough, bruising kisses, strong hands tangling in her hair, holding her prisoner with their painful grip.

'You wanted me last year—you used me—had your fun and left when you got bored. Now it's my turn—but I'll warn you, my darling Calypso...'

His savage snarl turned the endearment into a terrible epithet.

'I never——' Susannah began, but her voice failed her abruptly. Hadn't she admitted to herself that, in a way, she had used him, as a form of escape from her unhappiness?

'A week may have been long enough for you, but I doubt if it will be the same for me. I reckon I'll need longer than that—much longer! In fact, I don't think I'll *ever* get enough of you!'

CHAPTER NINE

THE hotel was very still and silent, most of the guests downstairs at an evening of folk music, and Susannah found herself hesitating uncertainly outside Mark's room, her newly fired resolve seeping from her as she stood with her hand half raised to knock. She would have much preferred to face him somewhere else—by the pool, or in the garden at the rear of the hotel—somewhere more public, less intimate, she thought, her mouth drying with nervous apprehension.

She had been surprised to learn from Theo that Mark had gone to his room early, and had been frankly unwilling to approach him there. At least his bedroom was here in Theo and Andrea's private accommodation this time, and not, as it had been last year, in one of the public rooms where both she and Mark had had to sleep because the manager's apartment was undergoing vital repairs—an indication, if only she had been able to see it, of the sort of problems Theo and Andi were already facing.

The thought of revisiting the room she had shared with him then was more than she could bear. In fact, perhaps she would do better to leave the whole thing until morning.

But deep down she knew that she couldn't let it wait. The conversation she had just had with Andrea had stunned her, her mind was reeling in confusion and disbelief, and she couldn't rest until she had tackled Mark about it. Drawing a deep breath and straightening her slim shoulders under the straps of the peach-coloured sundress into which she had changed for dinner, she lifted her hand again and knocked resolutely.

When there was no response, she thought at first that she hadn't been heard, or perhaps, she told herself hopefully, Theo had made a mistake and Mark had left

124

the hotel, possibly even driving into Valletta in search of some more sophisticated entertainment. Torn between cowardly relief and a sense of frustration, she was just about to turn away when the door swung open silently, making her jump like a startled cat.

'Well now, this *is* a surprise,' Mark drawled lazily, lounging against the door-frame, his long body indolently relaxed in loose-fitting cream trousers and a short-sleeved shirt which matched the golden colour of his eyes. 'To what do I owe the honour of this visit?'

He had worn exactly the same outfit at dinner, Susannah told herself furiously, so there was nothing new in his appearance, nothing to make her heart leap into a disturbingly uneven rhythm. But all the same she couldn't deny her instinctive response to the lean power of his body, the muscular strength of the forearms exposed by the short sleeves. He had obviously been relaxing, the shirt pulled loose at his narrow waist, and the soft fall of his bronze hair across his forehead combined with the sleepily sensual, heavy-lidded eyes to give him a slightly rumpled and vulnerable look which she found disturbingly appealing. But she would be all sorts of a fool to let herself be deceived by it; vulnerability was not a characteristic she thought of in connection with Mark Kingston.

'I . . .' she began, only to find that the dryness of her mouth was still troubling her, and unthinkingly she wetted her lips quickly to ease the discomfort, her nervousness increasing in leaps and bounds as she saw his tawny gaze drop downwards, his eyes narrowing disturbingly as he followed the tiny movement.

'I need to talk to you.' She brought the words out in a rush, sounding almost aggressive as a result.

One dark eyebrow drifted upwards in a carefully assumed expression of surprise and query in response to her tone, but he made no comment, instead straightening up slowly and letting the door swing fully open, one tanned hand sketching a gesture of invitation.

'Come in,' he said, and for the life of her she couldn't interpret the dry amusement that shaded his voice, seeing no possible reason for it, 'and tell me all about it.'

Beyond the open door, Susannah could see his shadowed room, lit only by the glow of a single bedside lamp, and all her confidence left her in a rush.

'Oh—I don't think—perhaps——' She broke off in confusion as the mockery she had sensed in his voice a moment before was physically expressed in the devilish smile which curled the corners of his lips.

'Afraid, Calypso?' he taunted softly, the false gentleness of his voice setting her teeth on edge.

'Not at all!' she declared indignantly. 'It's just...'

Once more the words failed her as she acknowledged that this corridor, so close to her sister's bedroom—and the baby's—was no place to hold the conversation she had planned to have with Mark. For one thing, it was getting close to the time for James' feed, and so Andrea might well be along at any moment. But the prospect of entering Mark's bedroom, of being alone with him there, revived all her memories of the times when she had shared his room—and his bed—so much more willingly, and by doing so seemed to commit her to more than she was prepared to give.

'You're quite safe.' Mark had seen the hesitation written on her face. 'I promise you I won't pounce unless specifically invited.'

His smile grew into a tigerish grin, one she hated on sight, as she detested the wicked glint in those golden eyes.

'Or have you decided that what you had to say isn't so very important after all?'

That note of mockery had become deliberate provocation now, and, hearing it, Susannah stiffened her spine, drawing on all her reserves of mental strength. What she had to say *was* important—doubly so if Andrea had been right, and that after tonight she would be free of this man's unwelcome attentions. Surely the prospect of that freedom was worth a few uncomfortable moments in his room?

That idea was so attractive that it brought a dramatic change in her mood, one that was mirrored in the wide, bright smile she turned on his watchful face as she shook her dark head.

'On the contrary,' she told him, her cheerfulness growing as she saw the way she had obviously disconcerted him by her reaction. 'You've just made me realise exactly how important it is.'

And, resolutely pushing away all trace of hesitancy in her mood, she stepped past him into the room, her movements briskly confident. Mark was like all bullies, she told herself. If you stood up to them, they backed down at once. At least, she hoped that was true.

'Take a seat.' Mark turned from closing the door and gestured towards the one chair in the room.

For a moment Susannah hovered indecisively. What she planned to say wouldn't take long, and she didn't want it to appear that she was planning on staying for any length of time. But then Mark himself moved to sit on the edge of the bed, and once more she had to change her mind. After all, she didn't want to antagonise him in any way, and standing stiffly in the middle of the room while he was seated made her feel disconcertingly tall and out of place, presenting an aggressive image which was not at all the one she thought Mark would accept, so, reluctantly, she followed his example and lowered herself into the seat.

'Would you like a drink?'

Mark was holding up a bottle of wine, tilting it towards an empty glass that stood on the dresser beside one that was already half-full. His cheerful courtesy grated on Susannah's painfully raw nerves. This wasn't a social call; she had come here to clarify the situation, not make polite small-talk . . .

'No.'

She regretted the single syllable as soon as it was out. For one thing, it sounded too curtly hostile, not a good move in the circumstances; and for another speaking had made her realise that her throat was still uncomfortably dry. Perhaps some alcohol would loosen her tongue, make it easier to speak.

'Well, all right. Perhaps just a small one—that's enough!' she added hastily, leaning forward in her seat, her hand outstretched—reaching, she suddenly realised, for Mark's arm to restrain him. For a second she froze into embarrassed stillness, her fingers just inches above

the sinewy, suntanned strength of his exposed forearm,
then abruptly he moved away from her.

'I have no intention of getting you drunk, Susannah!'
he snapped, his tone suddenly harsh.

'Of course not.' Susannah, still struggling to adjust
to the speed with which he had reacted, the violent rejection of her closeness, aimed for airy insouciance to
hide the way she was feeling, but was disturbed to find
that, instead of sounding carelessly nonchalant, the
words came out as brittle and condescending. 'I never
thought you were.'

Almost snatching the glass from his hand, she took a
hasty sip, one that turned into an unthinking gulp of the
cool wine as she heard Mark's response.

'I have never had to resort to the effects of alcohol to
get my women where I want them.'

'I suppose your mere presence—your sheer animal
magnetism—is enough to do the job for you!'

Susannah regretted the gibe as soon as it was out,
realising that the wine must have gone to her head much
more swiftly than she would have thought possible and
resolving to keep a careful check on her tongue in future.
When a small, slyly suggestive voice in the back of her
mind suggested that it was that 'women' which had stung
her into the sharp response, making her feel that she was
just one in a long line of conquests, she pushed it away
hastily. She had always known she was nothing special
to Mark; she had come to terms with that a long time
ago.

And this new development? Susannah was unprepared for the sudden stab of pain that came with the
realisation that not only was she in no way special to
Mark, in fact he had already lost all interest in her. If
what Andi had said was right, and she had no reason
to think that her sister had her facts wrong, Mark had
told Theo to arrange a meeting with his solicitor
tomorrow morning when the vital agreement would
finally be signed and become legally binding. She didn't
know what had brought about this change of heart, only
knew that she should be feeling a tremendous sense of
release, of being let off the hook, instead of which she
was a prey to a bitter sense of pique at the thought that

Mark hadn't needed the week that he had originally demanded. Instead, after only a few days, he had grown bored, obviously deciding that she wasn't worth the effort.

'If you say so.'

Mark refilled his own glass, then lounged back on the bed, supporting himself on one elbow, his long body as relaxed as the lazy drawl of his voice.

'I would prefer to put it down to chemistry—or electricity—whatever term you want to use to describe that special spark.'

Why had she never really noticed before just how attractive a voice Mark had? Susannah wondered, taking another, more careful, sip of her drink. It was low and rich, a voice that drew one's attention and held it, a voice she could listen to for hours. She gave a small sigh of relief as she felt some of the tension which had gripped her since she had first come looking for Mark leave her taut body, letting her breath escape softly as she leaned her head against the back of the chair, enjoying the feeling.

'That's better.' Mark's voice came from the shadows. 'You were like a cat on a hot tin roof when you first arrived. I'm quite harmless really,' he added, his voice deepening, becoming even more huskily enticing.

Privately, Susannah took the liberty of doubting that he was any such thing, but a strong sense of discretion warned her not to express her feelings out loud. To do so might result in his losing his temper, or drive him back into the bitterly hostile mood she had come to dread. Far better to keep him in this more relaxed, mellower frame of mind. At least this way she had more chance of getting a reasonable hearing.

'Just a great big pussycat,' she mocked gently, amazing herself with her easy response, allowing herself to relax a little more at the sound of the chuckle that was Mark's response to her light retort. 'Providing no one pulls your tail.'

'Exactly.' The single word was full of a lazy satisfaction—just the way a sleepy tiger might speak.

All the same, she would be wise to remember that, sleepy or not, the tiger was an efficient predator and possessed a set of vicious claws, Susannah warned herself. He might sound thoroughly indolent and contented right now, but she had little doubt that, if provoked, he would unleash the lethal energy that lay coiled beneath his relaxed pose—and spring.

'All you have to do is stroke me and I'll purr ecstatically.'

The sensual drawl of Mark's voice made Susannah think of rich honey oozing over gravel, and her brain threatened to blow a fuse at the contemplation of the possibility of indulging his suggestion of stroking the long, lean body sprawled out on the heavy cream cotton of the bedspread until he purred in contentment. In order to divert her wanton thoughts from the dangerously erotic path down which they seemed determined to go, she rushed into hasty speech.

'Do you remember that filthy stray who used to wander around the gardens?'

Uncertainty as to whether it was wise to revive memories of the previous year warred with a nervous need to say *something*, so that her voice sounded breathless and uneven, causing Mark to lift his head from the pillow and study her unnervingly closely, his eyes narrowing assessingly.

'Are you implying that I remind you of Melvyn the disgusting mog?'

The drawling tones were as deceptive as his loose-limbed pose, the dark thread of sardonic mockery running through them raising prickles of unease on Susannah's skin.

Only in his sexual habits, perhaps, Susannah thought privately, but she didn't dare express the comparison out loud.

'Oh, no—he was a real scruffy tom—smelly and dirty——'

'And half-starved,' Mark put in drily. 'So you, being the soft-hearted creature that you are, took him scraps from your meal every night.' His finely shaped mouth twisted into a wry grimace at the thought. 'The other guests must have been greatly entertained by his caterwauling when you didn't turn up.'

His teasing sounded gentler now, genuinely amused, and Susannah found herself relaxing once more. Or then again, perhaps it was the wine, combined with the fact that in the dimly lit room she could see so little of Mark's face, most of it in shadow, the fiercely probing eyes hidden from her.

'I couldn't let him go hungry!'

'Of course not,' Mark assured her lazily. 'But I wonder what Theo thought?'

'He must have decided that his new sister-in-law was a rabid carnivore—right down to the bones!'

Laughter bubbled in Susannah's voice as she recalled how, with Mark's helpful connivance, she had smuggled choice morsels from her plate, wrapped in a paper napkin, to feed the pathetic stray cat who had adopted her as its personal saviour. She hadn't missed the titbits anyway—she hadn't had much appetite then—at least, not for food!

'I wonder what happened to him,' she said hastily, once more needing to distract her mind from disturbing memories. 'I suppose he starved——'

Mark gave a swift snort of laughter.

'Not on your life! You obviously haven't been down to the kitchens lately. If you had, you'd see one very sleek and contented feline installed officially as the resident rodent controller—your sister is every bit as soft as you are.'

He made it sound as if he meant the words physically, his low, caressing tones seeming to slide over Susannah's skin like warm cream, and she found that her heartbeat had quickened perceptibly, making her breath come unevenly so that she was sure Mark must hear its rapid ebb and flow.

'I'm glad he's happy...'

'Well, at least *he's* glad that you came here last year.'

To Susannah's distress, the bite of acid was back in Mark's voice, all the more painful because of those few moments of warmth and gentleness, making her flinch inwardly. God, but he was eaten up with bitterness!

'Do you blame me?'

To her consternation, she realised that she had spoken her thoughts out loud.

'No one likes being used.'

'Used!' Susannah's voice was high and shrill—a mistake, she realised as the long body on the bed tensed, losing all its earlier indolence in a split second. 'No one *used . . .*'

Her voice failed her, drying to an embarrassing croak as she forced herself to face facts. Hadn't she flung herself into an affair with Mark in order to try and forget about Simon? With strict honesty, couldn't that be described as using him?

'If there was any using, it was mutual,' she managed clumsily, her tongue seeming suddenly thick and awkward in her mouth. 'We both used each other—got what we wanted from the relationship—some pleasant times——'

'Pleasant!' Mark repeated, a dangerous edge to his voice, his lips twisting around the word as if it had a poisonous taste in his mouth. 'So you do admit that there was some pleasure in our being together?' he went on in a very different tone, and as he spoke he moved again, sitting forward, swinging his long legs to the floor.

'Of course!' Susannah declared, on a note of something approaching desperation. She would be a fool to deny such a thing; after all, he had seen the evidence with his own eyes.

She was suddenly profoundly thankful for the deep shadows in the room; they concealed the burning colour that flooded into her cheeks at the thought of the wanton way she had behaved in this man's arms, her sighs, her little moans of delight, the way she had pleaded, cajoled, and, at times, actually begged for his caresses, his possession. She could almost hear inside her head her final, ecstatic cries at the culmination of their lovemaking, as the mind-blowing force of the experience took her over the edge into a world of total sensation.

Once again she knew a sense of deep relief for the fact that this was a very different room from the one they had shared then. She almost felt as if the sounds of their lovemaking, the movements of their shadows, might have been imprinted on the walls, lingering there to haunt her.

'Of course . . .'

Mark turned his face so that the light of the moon, coming through the open window, shone directly on to it, draining all the colour from those golden eyes, making them seem dark and infinitely disturbing.

'You can't deny the pleasure you felt.' It was a statement, not a question, an arrogant declaration of total certainty with the hateful stamp of possessiveness on it.

'No, I can't!'

She felt totally confused, her nerves on edge, making coherent thought almost impossible. When Andrea had told her that Mark was ready to sign the contract, she had thought that meant that he was no longer interested in an affair with her, but he wasn't behaving as if that was the case.

'I *can't*—I won't!' she flung at him. 'But it's over— done with—at least, it will be when you sign those papers tomorrow——'

'So Andi's told you the good news.'

'Y-yes.' Why did she suddenly get the feeling that, after all, it wasn't such good news, for her at least? 'So our agreement's over.'

She couldn't believe it when he shook his head, a faint, infinitely disturbing smile at the corners of his mouth.

'Oh, no, Calypso, I'm not letting you off the hook that easily.'

'But...' When she had told herself that he no longer wanted her, his response was as inexplicable as it was unexpected. 'But you have to—why can't you see that?'

'Because I don't want to.'

When she had been expecting forcefulness, anger even, Mark's response was almost frighteningly gentle. Just so must Dracula have spoken, in just such a voice, Susannah thought fearfully. With just that soft enticement in his tone he would have hypnotised his victim, holding her transfixed, unable to resist his fatal attack. He would have kept her mesmerised by the sheer force of his personality—and then he would move in for the kill.

'I told you before, Calypso—I don't want it to end. I didn't then—I don't now. I want you——'

'*No*!'

The force of Susannah's declaration pushed her to her feet in a movement so violent that just for a second she swayed, unable to regain her balance. In immediate response, in one, lithe, elegant uncoiling of his long body, Mark stood up too, reaching out to steady her, his hard fingers seeming to burn her skin so that she flinched away, convinced that his touch had actually branded her, like some slave of long ago. Mentally, he had already done that, she thought miserably, marking her out as his on a hot April morning twelve months before.

'No!' she said again, twisting away from him. She couldn't take any more of this; she was going, leaving before she finally broke down.

Becoming aware of the fact that her glass was still in her hand, she looked round her dazedly, wanting somewhere to put it out of the way. When Mark held out his hand to her, she thought he meant to take it from her, and automatically responded.

Too late, she realised her mistake, saw what he had planned, far too late to take any evasive action. With the swift movement of a striking snake he snatched the glass, tossed it disdainfully aside, heedless of where it fell, then captured her wrists in a punishing grip, holding her prisoner with a contemptuous ease.

'I want you,' he repeated, his voice thickening in a way that made Susannah shudder in unwanted response. 'I want you—and you want me—why else would you be here?'

And then, far, far too late, Susannah recalled his husky whisper in the dark, on the ferry, his urgent 'Calypso, come to me tonight—let it be like it used to be.'

With a terrible sense of despair, born of the realisation of how foolish she had been, she saw her visit to Mark's room through his eyes, and knew that all the time, while she had believed him to be relaxed and approachable, waiting for her to tell him why she had come, he had not been like that at all.

'I only bet on certainties,' he had said, and in his mind he had been so sure of her that he had even thrown away his trump card, removing the threat to Theo and Andi so that she couldn't claim that he had forced her in any way. Or was that just another of his power games, believing that by this unexpected change of tack, his apparent generosity, he would win her over where threats had failed?

All along, he had thought he knew exactly why she was there, and, as he had said earlier, had been content to wait, to let anticipation sharpen his appetite. Like the tiger she had accused him of resembling, he had been lying, apparently lazily indolent, while all the time each powerful muscle had in fact been tensed, his whole body waiting for the perfect moment in which to pounce—and now, it seemed, that moment had come.

'I know I promised not to pounce unless invited,' Mark told her softly, that hateful smile growing more darkly triumphant with each word. 'But truthfully, my darling Calypso, isn't the fact that you're here an invitation in itself?'

CHAPTER TEN

'No!' SUSANNAH tried again, on a very different note, horrified to find that even in her own ears her voice lacked conviction. 'I came here to *talk*!'

'Of course.'

Mark's smile dismissed her attempts at explanation with a mocking condescension.

'I'm as aware of the need for sexual manners as you. After all, we're not animals—we can't just rip each other's clothes off before we've said hello. A little conversation—a glass of wine...'

His eyes went to the discarded glass, then swung back to lock with her wide, shocked indigo gaze, holding her still with a mesmeric force from which she couldn't break away.

'Are all pleasant social conventions. And a slight delay—— ' his voice deepened, becoming sensually husky in a way that sent a *frisson* of awareness shivering down Susannah's spine '—like a fine aperitif, awakens the taste buds—stimulates the appetite——'

Susannah couldn't suppress a gasp of shock at the blatant way he spoke in terms of appetite and taste. She was well aware of the fact that Mark wasn't talking about a need for food but of a hunger of a very different kind, and the fact that he described it as an appetite—simply an animal desire to be appeased without a second thought—revealed only too clearly, if she had needed any further evidence, the fact that he felt no emotional spark at all.

'But I can't keep my mind on stray cats or any other topic of polite conversation when you're sitting there in that devastating slip of a dress, looking every inch the siren——'

'Oh, now you're being ridiculous!'

136

Nervous tension made Susannah's voice shake, her dry throat giving her words a betraying huskiness that, seeing Mark's eyes darken until they were almost all black, only a tiny rim of gold at the edge, she realised with a sense of horror he had interpreted as encouragement.

He was still holding her hand, she realised, and as she struggled to defuse the heightened atmosphere she felt him slowly begin to move his thumb round and round in the centre of her palm, the soft brush of skin against skin making her heart clench painfully, shivers of response radiating outward and up her arm like some intense electric shock. In the next second it was as if the rest of her body had become insubstantial, as if her whole being was centred on that tiny point of contact, the delicate, rhythmic caress a source of intense delight, driving all rational thought from her mind. With a wrenching effort she swallowed hard and tried again.

'Everyone knows that sirens are small, delicate creatures with long blonde hair...'

Her voice failed as Mark adamantly shook his head, increasing his thumb's pressure on her hand very slightly.

'You're thinking of mermaids,' he murmured softly, his tawny head bent, his face coming very close to Susannah's, his breath warm on her cheek as his voice sank even lower, becoming a huskily enticing whisper. 'I see sirens as being tall, long-legged women...'

His eyes swept over her body in a survey that was as sensual as a caress, and to her consternation Susannah found herself reacting as if his scrutiny had actually had a physical form, swaying slightly, her legs feeling soft as cotton wool, too weak to support her. Inside her head a tiny, rational part of her brain was aware of the danger she was in, knew she should move, that to stay like this wasn't safe or in the least wise. But it seemed that she had lost the ability to direct her limbs, as if her muscles had atrophied until they were incapable of action. If Mark had bound her hand and foot with steel wires, he couldn't have held her captive more successfully—and yet their only point of contact was that fragile linking of their fingers, the soft movement of his thumb continuing with hypnotic effect.

'Mark...'

She had meant it as a protest. In the hazy depths of her brain where she had formed his name it had sounded that way, but, strangely, once out in the open, it seemed worryingly, even to her own ears, like an expression of sensual arousal, a breathy sigh of encouragement, an invitation...

'Sirens have hair like polished ebony silk...'

The strong, tanned fingers of his free hand slid through the soft strands of her hair, setting her scalp tingling, and when they lingered at the nape of her neck she drew in her breath sharply, intensely aware of their strength, of the way just the slightest increase in their pressure could mean all the difference between pleasure and pain.

Catching the tiny, betraying evidence of her involuntary reaction, Mark smiled slowly, triumph lighting in his eyes, the thumb at the base of her skull moving in a subtle, erotic pattern that matched his caress of her palm, and in spite of herself Susannah murmured in delighted response.

'And they have smooth, golden limbs...'

At last her hand was released, Mark's smile growing wider at her faint whimper of protest, and his warm palms slid down the lightly tanned skin of her arms.

'Deep, deep blue eyes, the colour of the sea around these islands...'

His voice was an enchanter's instrument, weaving a deep, hypnotic spell around her from which she could not break free.

'A siren's lips are full and soft—so ripe for kissing...'

Mark's words were breathed against her mouth, the brief intensity of his kiss awakening a yearning need deep inside her, a feeling like the fluttering of a thousand butterfly wings in the pit of her stomach.

'And her body is shaped for love.'

Susannah had to strain to hear the last words, so soft was his whisper, little more than a sigh. She felt as though the room and its furnishings, all her surroundings, had faded into a hazy blur. She no longer seemed to be standing but was floating, carried along on a warm, golden sea. It was as if the cool light of the moon that bathed the room had suddenly taken on the glowing power of the sun, flooding her body with its heat. Her

mind glowed too, feeling as intoxicated as if each word
that Mark had spoken had been a sip of sparkling wine
fed to her from a delicate crystal glass.

In this mood of newly heightened awareness, the gentle
smoothing movement of his hands down the slender lines
of her body, lingering heartbreakingly briefly on the soft
swell of her breasts, the curves of her hips, was a further
intensification of her pleasure, raising the temperature
of her blood higher and higher with each caress, burning
away all thought so that she didn't rouse herself from
her trance even when those long brown hands moved to
the large cream buttons that formed a line down the front
of her sundress.

'This dress is pure temptation,' he murmured, in a
voice that was thick with passion. 'It just begs to be
removed—and I...'

The first button slid from its fastening, the warm brush
of his fingers against her breast a delight so powerful it
stabbed straight to her heart like a pain, jolting her out
of the golden intoxication that held her spellbound and
into cold, shocked awareness of just what was happening.

'...I cannot resist temptation——'

'Stop!'

Her voice sounded rusty, weak and rough as if she
hadn't used it for months, and even she had to admit,
if only to herself, that it held no conviction. Mark didn't
even hesitate, sliding his fingers down to the next button
and easing it open with infinite care.

'Never could...'

Susannah's head swam as if she were in the grip of
some fever. She was drunk—on one glass of wine!—or
fainting—or delirious—the shafts of pleasure searing
through her body made her dig her teeth into her lower
lip to bite back a cry of pure delight. But no restraint
was possible when Mark's head lowered, his warm lips
caressing the delicate flesh his hands had exposed as she
moaned her need aloud, the sound so primitive, so alien,
that it shocked her into an agonising clarity of thought.

'Mark—I said *stop*!'

That sounded more convincing, panic giving her voice
an edge that it hadn't had before, but for all the effect
it had on Mark she might not have spoken. Deliberately

trailing the back of his hand down the creamy curve of her right breast, he let those determined fingers head, agonisingly inexorably, for the next fastening.

'I—*no*!'

Grabbing his wrists, she struggled to still those erotically tormenting hands, her efforts so pitifully ineffectual that she knew she would have to resort to other methods—but what? And then, just when she was about to give in to panic, desperation gave her the weapon she needed.

'Mark—listen—I really did come here to talk——'

'Sure——'

'But I did—I wanted to talk about Simon!'

That stopped him dead. If she had flung a live, hissing poisonous snake straight in his face it couldn't have had a more violent effect, making him withdraw from her sharply, the flush of arousal fading from his face leaving it bleak and hard, his eyes cold as ice.

'Simon,' he said harshly, the name sounding like an epithet or a curse. His hands fell to his sides, held stiffly away from his body, as if he felt that the taint he had absorbed by touching her might contaminate him further.

'Yes—Simon. I wanted to talk about him,' Susannah repeated shakenly, needing to make sure the message had got through to him even though it was obvious from his reaction that it needed no further reinforcement.

But she had to keep talking, do something to distract herself from the terrible emptiness that seemed to have invaded her body, draining all the heat from her veins, leaving her feeling devastatingly drained and totally bereft. And it was true, after all. When Andi had told her that Mark was going to sign the contracts, she had promised herself that if it was true, if she was really off the hook once and for all, then she would tell him about Simon, and the real reason why she had left without a word last year. She owed him that at least.

'You have to listen.'

'Why?' The black anger had gone, leaving just a blank, emotionless flatness that was somehow more terrible than his earlier cold fury. 'What the hell do you think you could tell me about him that I could possibly want to know?'

Having won his attention so completely, Susannah now found herself wishing that he would look anywhere but at her. Still, at least his hard-eyed gaze was only fixed on her *face*. She was painfully, shamefully aware of the amount of golden-toned skin exposed by the open front of her dress, the swell of her breasts still flushed from his attentions. She felt desperately vulnerable and exposed in more ways than one, but didn't dare lift her fingers to the buttons, even to close them, for fear of drawing those cold, eagle's eyes back to the part of her body which had so recently absorbed him. If she did, she was quite sure that their trembling would reveal her inner turmoil, betraying the mask of calm which she was struggling to maintain as the sham it was.

'I—I wanted to explain...'

What had happened to the resolve and confidence of earlier that evening? When she had left Andi, she had been completely certain that all she had to do was simply to talk to Mark, to let him know how things had really been with Simon, and he would understand. But that had been when she thought his agreement on the contracts meant that he had lost interest in her. But his behaviour a few moments before had shown her earlier certainty to be a foolish delusion.

Looking into Mark's strongly sculpted face, where hostility and rejection were stamped so clearly that it was as if steel shutters had slammed shut behind his eyes, she had to force herself to stand her ground before the burning intensity of his gaze. There was no warmth in his look, for all that it was almost translucent; instead it cut into her with the force of a sword of ice.

'Explain away.'

The response was thrown away, flung at her with a laconic indifference that was like the lash of a whip in her face. She found herself almost wishing for a return to his earlier anger. At least then he had been feeling *something*. Now it seemed that no emotion, not even hatred, could ever touch the cold-hearted devil before her.

'I——'

'But before you start,' he broke in on her, 'do me a favour.'

Absurdly—crazily—her foolish heart actually leapt, and she had to bite down hard on the impulsive 'Anything!' that almost escaped her. She was intensely grateful that she had managed to suppress the unthinking response a moment later when those icy eyes swept over her, scathingly contemptuous, lingering insolently on the shadowed valley between her exposed breasts.

'Fasten yourself up.' It was an order, a command as arrogant as an emperor's snap of his fingers at a slave, and it was accompanied by another insultingly disdainful flick of his eyes to take in her dishevelled state. 'If what you have to tell me is so important, you wouldn't want me to be——' the deliberately sneering pause brought burning colour rushing into Susannah's cheeks '—distracted, would you?'

'Why, you——!'

Face flaming, blue eyes blazing, Susannah took a hasty step forwards, her hand coming up, fingers spread wide for maximum impact, aiming at a lean, bronzed cheek, wanting to wipe that hateful smile from his face. But her attack was forestalled with insulting ease, her hand captured once more in his, but this time in a way that was totally different from his earlier soft caress. Hard, cruel fingers closed tightly round her wrist, gripping it with such force that she feared the fragile bones might actually splinter under the pressure exerted on it.

'Now, now,' he admonished softly. 'Resorting to violence is a sign of a second-rate mind. And really, you have no right to object,' he added, the ominously soft voice laced with a silky menace that made Susannah shiver in horror. 'After all, I'm only giving you a taste of your own medicine.'

The smile that curled the corners of his mouth in response to her puzzled expression was not in the least pleasant. In fact, Susannah found it the most hateful and sickeningly insincere response she had ever seen, having nothing to do with approachability or humour, but motivated solely by cynical triumph and cruel satisfaction.

'It isn't pleasant being used and then discarded, is it, my lovely Calypso?'

'I didn't——' Susannah began, but Mark wouldn't let her finish.

'So tell me about Simon,' he cut in coldly, letting her hand drop so suddenly and roughly that it jarred her shoulder sickeningly. 'I really am fascinated to learn what it was about this man that he had such power over you— so that he only had to call and you came running.'

'It wasn't like that!'

Her body functioning on automatic pilot, her actions bearing no relation to her thoughts, Susannah lifted her hands to the front of her dress, fumbling hopelessly with the buttons, trying and failing to fasten them up again.

'I—I...'

Earlier, on her way to Mark's room, she had gone over and over in her mind exactly what she wanted to say, shaping her explanation as carefully as possible— but now all those carefully chosen words, the well thought out phrases, had deserted her and her mind was just a terrified blank.

'How *was* it, darling?' Mark's tone managed to turn the endearment into a biting insult. 'What was it that made this Simon so very special? How was it for you with him?'

Another of those hatefully humourless smiles made it obvious that the sexual innuendo was deliberately meant. Then, as Susannah hunted for the words to answer him, he reached out once more and caught hold of her hand again, stilling her futile struggle with the buttons, and drawing her slowly and inexorably towards him.

'Tell me about Simon, Susannah,' he cajoled softly, each word seeming to fall like a freezing drop of water on to her spine and slide slowly, shiveringly downwards. 'Was he good for you—in bed, I mean? Could he light the fire inside you the way I can? Did you come to life in his arms, my beauty, as you did in mine? Did you moan and writhe, and sigh your pleasure out loud—did you beg for his touch as you——?'

'Stop it! Stop it!' Susannah whimpered, her voice just a thin thread of sound, and she couldn't be sure whether Mark hadn't heard her or was simply ignoring her pleading as he continued his cruel litany.

'As you did for me last year? Did you offer him the wonderful, sexy body that you gave to me so willingly, my dark siren? Could he make you melt with desire—burn with need—cry aloud in ecstasy?'

'No! Oh, no, no, no!'

Desperately Susannah shook her head, the violence of her movement as much to drive away the darkly erotic images his words were creating in her mind as to emphasise her denial. Looking anywhere but into his taunting face, she blinked furiously to force back the tears that burned in her eyes, threatening to spill over and pour down her cheeks.

It was precisely because it had not been like that with Simon that she had felt so badly about her affair with Mark. Having learned her lesson early, knowing that sex without love was not for her, she had been convinced that true sexual happiness would result from a relationship in which she had come to know her partner fully, to care for him in every way possible. So she had found it impossible to come to terms with the fact that, even though she had known Simon for years, and had respected and admired him, he had never aroused in her the sort of passion that Mark Kingston, a total stranger, had been able to awaken with just the touch of one finger, a single kiss. It seemed that he knew exactly which buttons to press to create the response he wanted, and he had taken full advantage of the fact.

'Don't tell me—it was one of those amazing, cerebral relationships where your minds were in perfect unity.'

Susannah had actually opened her mouth to say yes, she and Simon had shared something very special, when the truth hit her like a flash of lightning, closing her lips on the angry retort. Uncomfortable as it was to face it, even though they had been together for some time, even though she would have said that she cared very much for him, she and Simon had never shared the feeling of being perfectly in tune with each other that, for some of the time at least, she had experienced with Mark during the trip to Mdina, and again on Gozo. If she was strictly honest, although they got on well together, she and Simon had few interests in common except for their work at the leisure centre which was what had brought

them together in the first place. Simon would never have
enjoyed exploring the ruined temples at Ggantija, and
he would much rather have gone deep-sea fishing than
spent time in the Silent City. And Simon would never
have discussed a major project like the Victoria with her.
Perhaps, in a way, that was one of the reasons why she
felt so uncomfortable about her promotion. Deep down,
she knew that Simon really hadn't thought her capable
of more than the job she was already doing.

'No——'

'No?'

Was it shock, triumph or simply blank disbelief that
shaded Mark's voice now? Susannah was beyond deciding, incapable of interpreting the look in his eyes. In
fact, she was no longer even able to understand her own
reaction because when rationally she knew that she
should be feeling fear and rejection of this man, when
she should be struggling to free herself, she now only
knew that her real emotions were in fact the opposite of
what she might expect. She didn't want to be free. The
only feeling that gripped her was a yearning to be in his
arms, a longing for him to kiss her. She wanted to feel
his lips on hers, the pressure of his strong body against
hers, and she wanted it more than she had ever wanted
anything in her life.

'Tell me about Simon,' Mark insisted.

'We—were going to be married.'

It was a struggle to force her mind to focus on the
words, but she *had* to concentrate. If she didn't, there
was the worrying possibility that she might actually put
her body's needs into words, might demand that he hold
her, beg him to kiss her...

'Or, at least, that was what everyone thought, and
then...'

'He jilted you?' Mark supplied when she found it too
difficult to go on.

'No...'

Was that the only explanation he could think of, that
she had been jilted and on the rebound had fallen into
bed with him? Would that have made her behaviour
easier to understand? Would she have felt better about
herself if it had been the case?

'I just realised that I couldn't marry him; what I felt wasn't strong enough. I thought it was—we'd been together for nearly two years—but when he finally asked me I just knew I couldn't say yes. I knew it would be wrong to do so—that I didn't care for him *enough*—not in that way. It would never have worked. I realised I wasn't ready to settle down—that there were so many things I'd never tried—experiences I'd never had. Simon—took it badly——' Her voice shook on the blatant understatement. 'It made things very difficult at work—he was a senior instructor at the leisure centre. So I came on holiday to get away from it all—and met you.'

'And met me,' Mark echoed darkly. 'And I was one of those things you'd never tried—an experience you'd never had...'

Susannah winced at the bite of acid in his words, wishing she could deny them, but honesty made that impossible.

'But then Simon phoned...'

'He wanted me to go to him...'

Susannah's voice was very low. She couldn't quite bring herself to say that it hadn't actually been *Simon* who had phoned her, but her father. Remembering, it was as if she was living through the experience a second time, once more enduring the terrible sense of shock that had felt like a blow to her head, making her mind reel as she took in what was being said.

'It was important to get there as quickly as possible. I—forgot all about you.'

That was a mistake—a *bad* mistake—she realised, as Mark's face whitened in fury, his anger drawing his skin tight over his cheekbones, and making those eagle's eyes burn translucently. It wasn't accurate, either. It was true that in those first stunned moments after she had put the phone down she had been unable to think of anything other than getting away, finding a flight with a free seat and flying back to England, but once that had been organised, the first thing she had thought of was telling Mark. She had even gone to his room to find him, only recalling, when she found it empty, that he had gone out with Theo on a trip to Valletta and wasn't expected back until late afternoon.

Susannah's face clouded, her dark eyes becoming dull with remembered pain at the thought of what had happened next. Because it had been when she opened a drawer in the desk in Mark's room, looking for some paper on which to write an explanatory note, that she had made the discovery that, when combined with the things she had overheard earlier, which until now had been pushed from her mind by events, brought home to her just how deceived she had been and that Mark's behaviour had never been anything more than the act that, not knowing she was listening, he had described it as.

Since she had met Mark she had been so completely swept up in the maelstrom of physical passion that they created between them that she wouldn't even have paused to consider the question of protection if Mark hadn't taken care of it. It had never occurred to her to question the ease with which, even in this strongly Catholic country, he had been able to do so. She had simply been deeply mortified by her own irresponsibility and grateful for the fact that Mark hadn't shared her failing. But now, seeing the bundle of small, foil-wrapped parcels in the drawer, she was forced to reconsider.

'I wasn't looking for this,' Mark had said, and she had believed him, just as she had also believed him when he had assured her that their meeting had knocked him off balance as much as it had her, or that he wasn't usually so precipitate in rushing into a relationship. She had been naïvely pleased by his comments, believing that they made her special to him, not just some casual relationship, and she had been frankly flattered by the thought that she could have had the same sort of effect on this devastatingly attractive man as he had had on her, that his behaviour had been as spontaneous and emotional as hers.

But now she was forced to realise just how blind she had been, to admit that here before her was the evidence of just how coldly prepared Mark had been; evidence of the way that, on holiday, he had—expected, maybe—hoped, certainly—that something like this would happen.

This wasn't just the responsible behaviour of some
mature and thoughtful man who, as a sensible pre-
caution, carried one or two condoms with him. This sort
of preparation was only carried out by someone who
anticipated—*counted on*—an active sex life of the sort,
she admitted, fiery colour flaming in her cheeks, that he
had enjoyed over the past few days. Mark had come on
holiday, as she supposed many men would, looking for
a holiday fling, a casual, uncommitted, purely sexual
relationship—not that there was anything *pure* about the
way he had behaved. He had probably picked her out
from the start—after all, there weren't many young, un-
attached women staying at the hotel—and had calcu-
latedly set about seducing her just as a tiger carefully
stalked its prey, and, already mentally off balance because of Simon's behaviour, she hadn't offered much
resistance—in fact she had positively flung herself into
his arms, and his bed. He must have thought all his
birthdays had come at once, she thought on a wave of
bitter self-disgust. He'd probably anticipated that he
would have to expend a lot more energy, time and money
in order to charm her, win her over. Instead, she'd done
most of the running for him!

'You *forgot*!'

Mark repeated her foolhardy words in a dangerously
quiet voice, one that made all the tiny hairs on the back
of Susannah's neck lift in fearful apprehension. Nervously she recalled his response to her declaration of
boredom. If she had stung his male pride then, she had
done far more damage to it now.

'*You forgot*!' he said again, the savage threat in his
voice making her stomach clench painfully, a sound of
distress escaping her as the hard fingers that grasped her
wrist tightened bruisingly, his other hand coming up to
close over her arm. 'Do you know—do you have the
faintest bloody idea how I felt when I got back to the
hotel and found you gone?'

Probably very much as he felt now, with his macho
pride burning at the thought that his sexual conquest,
his holiday entertainment, had got away from him.

'You were probably furious that I got in first!' she
flung at him, praying that her defiant tone, the flash of

her indigo eyes, hid the way she was quailing pitifully inside. 'Because I'm sure that was the plan, wasn't it? That when the two weeks of my holiday were up you'd be on your way without a backward glance.'

'There wasn't any plan——'

'Oh, come on, Mark! Don't put on the hard-done-by act!'

If anyone was entitled to feel that way, then surely it was herself. Strangely, it hurt more that he was still persisting with the pretence that he *had* been acting purely spontaneously than if he had admitted straight out that she was right in her interpretation of events. Once more she acknowledged that she should really be grateful for the way things had turned out. At least that way she had managed to preserve the tiny, tattered bit of self-respect that was still left to her.

'I left you a note.'

'So you did.' It was a low, menacing growl. '"Gotta go—'bye! It was fun",' he quoted savagely, and Susannah had to impose strict self-control not to wince visibly. Spoken out loud, it sounded even more flippantly careless than, still smarting from her discovery, she had planned at the time.

'You wanted to be the one who said goodbye?'

Defiance was another mistake, she admitted, as a muscle jerked violently in Mark's jaw, his eyes narrowing to mere golden slits in the hard, set mask that was his face.

'At least I didn't forget you compl——'

Her voice died abruptly, frozen into silence by the way his head went back, the blaze of fury in his eyes. Privately she cursed her foolish use of that over-emotive word.

'You may have *forgotten* me last year,' he muttered in a voice that was thickened and rough, 'but I'll make damn sure it won't happen again.'

Susannah would have said that it was impossible for his grip on her wrist to tighten any more, but now she felt a very real fear that her bones might actually snap under his savage pressure, and she whimpered slightly in genuine pain.

'Mark—please...'

'Mark—please,' he echoed mockingly, matching her trembling intonation with deadly accuracy. 'Please what, my lovely? What is it you want from me, Calypso?'

'Please . . .' She couldn't control her voice and it broke awkwardly on the single word. 'You're—you're hurting me . . .'

But even as she spoke she knew that the pain in her wrist was as nothing to the one in her heart. Foolishly, crazily, pathetically, deep down inside her, some deluded part of her mind had still actually hoped that she had been wrong, both last year and again this time. She had never actually shut the door on him, as she had believed, but had left it open just a tiny crack in the naïve hope that he would convince her that what they had shared had, after all, been more than a passing fancy, or, as she had described it with brutal realism, just an itch that had to be scratched.

But now, looking into Mark's face, seeing the dark cruelty stamped on it, the cold, emotionless sensuality that burned in his eyes, she knew she had only scratched the surface of the ruthless predator that was Mark Kingston and she shivered fearfully, her apprehension made all the worse by the certainty that the involuntary little movement would not escape that watchful eagle's gaze.

And of course it didn't.

'Are you cold?' he asked, in a voice that rang with such a convincing note of concern that for a second she was conned into believing that he actually felt something, and stared at him in blank confusion. 'We'll have to do something about that—find a way to warm you up—come here . . .'

And before Susannah could focus her bruised and numbed brain clearly enough to anticipate what he had in mind and take evasive action, he moved swiftly to gather her close, enfolding her in his arms and drawing her up against the hard length of his body. At last he released that punishing grip on her wrist, his hands moving to her shoulders, warm palms sliding softly over her skin, awakening every nerve, every cell until she was murmuring an incoherent, uncontrollable response.

'Better now?' he whispered, his breath feathering her cheek. 'Warmer?'

If the truth were told, she was too warm, hot blood coursing through her veins in response to the pounding of her heart so that she felt as if her body were on fire, her bones seeming to melt in its heat until she was leaning weakly against him, unable to resist as one of those strong, tanned hands moved upwards, cupping her chin, lifting her face to his.

'Oh, Calypso...'

The husky whisper was working its magic again, weaving around her thoughts, capturing her mind and holding it mesmerised, unable to think of anything beyond Mark and the sensual enchantment he was creating.

'No matter what you say, I know you could never have forgotten this...'

His mouth brushed hers, heartbreakingly briefly, and she felt rather than heard the laughter deep in his throat as, unable to stop herself, she gave a small murmur of protest as his head lifted again.

'Or this...'

His arms tightened round her, driving the breath from her body as he crushed her even harder against him, leaving her in no doubt about the urgency of his desire for her, his hands burning a heated trail down her back, over the curves of her hips and the slim length of her thighs, bringing her so close—and yet not close enough.

'And this...'

This time his kiss was a savage assault on her mouth, ravaging her lips and her senses, and yet even that was not enough. Every nerve in her body was stirring, clamouring its need, and she flung up her arms, burying her fingers in the bronze silk of his hair and pulling his head down even closer, her mouth opening under the pressure of his to allow the intimate invasion of his tongue, her small, incoherent murmurs encouraging and exciting him in a way no spoken words ever could.

She was so absorbed in her own feelings, in the aching yearning that blazed and flamed inside her, that she barely felt his fingers move to her dress, easily dispensing with the few remaining buttons, only becoming aware of his actions as the peach cotton whispered down her body, pooling on the floor at her feet.

'And I know you remember this...'

She felt the heat of his breath on the highly sensitised flesh of her breasts, her own breath catching in her throat as she tensed expectantly, waiting for its warm touch to be followed by the burning heat of his hands, and, a few agonising seconds later, by the hot demand of his mouth, seeming to draw out her very soul as he suckled fiercely.

'Mark...'

His name was a shaken cry, her sense of wonder, the growing, spiralling longing needing some vocal expression even though she was past forming any coherent words. But Mark needed no help in interpreting her feelings, gathering her up and carrying her towards the bed, flinging off his own clothes before he joined her, drawing her to him once more and using the magic of his touch, his kisses, to bring her to a state of mindless delirium in which the only thing she was aware of was him, his hands and his mouth, and the glorious sensations they were triggering in her body.

He had always been a generous lover. In the past, becoming aware of her own inexperience, he had always made sure that she was as aroused as he was, holding back on his own needs in order to give her pleasure, and this time was no exception. But now there was a very different feeling to every move, every caress, every kiss. It was as if he were determined to stamp himself on every inch of her body, burn his imprint into her mind, as he roused her to such heights of delight that her longing for his final possession was a need so sharp it was intense as pain. Again and again he brought her to a point so near to the full knowledge of his lovemaking, only to make her wait yet again.

'Oh, please...' Driven to the end of endurance, the words escaped in a desperate rush. 'Mark, please—please...'

Only then did he move over her, gathering her restless body up in his arms, a small, triumphant laugh escaping him as he felt the way she strained against him, communicating physically the yearning that was beyond words.

'Oh, yes, my darling Calypso...' His muttered words were harsh with a passion to match her own. 'Whatever else happens, you'll always remember this...'

And then at last he released her from the torment of waiting, her wild cry of delight at the moment of his possession echoed by his own gasping moan of response before the violent force of mutual feeling overtook them, driving them relentlessly, gloriously, inevitably towards the mind-shattering culmination that was like a golden explosion inside her head, his name a litany of joy on her lips as slowly, so very slowly, she drifted back to reality again.

'Oh, Calypso...'

Mark's voice was uneven as he flung himself on to his back, his sweat-slicked chest rising and falling with each deep, ragged breath, one arm flung up to cover his eyes.

'You see,' he said, in a tone rich with satisfaction, 'that's what it was like—what I can't forget. The magic is still there, my sexy little siren. *That* is something you'll not forget so easily.'

'Forget?' Susannah echoed dreamily, her voice just a breath, a sigh of exhausted contentment. 'Never.'

She didn't care what she was saying, what it might reveal to him. Her control over her mind and body was gone, torn to shreds and then burned up in the sensual storm which had assailed her.

'*Never!*' she sighed again, and felt the bed shake with Mark's silent laughter.

'And I'd bet everything I own that not a single thought of dear Simon ever entered your head,' he declared on a note of dark triumph.

Simon. The name stabbed straight to Susannah's heart like an ice-cold knife, slashing through the dreamy haze which clouded her mind. It was true that she had never thought of him. When she had been capable of the thought, which had been only in rare moments of surfacing from the tumult of sensation that had possessed her, her mind had been aware only of Mark, his body, his voice, his hands and lips and the delightful pleasures they were creating.

But now a feeling like the splash of icy water in her face jolted her painfully back to reality with the realisation that if she had ever needed proof that she had never really, truly, loved Simon, then she had just been given it. The kisses she and Simon had shared had been gentle, warm, affectionate, but in contrast to the blazing heat of the passion she and Mark had shared they appeared as less than tepid. Simon had loved her, but she hadn't been able to give him what he had needed and so, in the end, she had broken his heart. Recalling the full truth of what had happened, the terrible details she hadn't been able to tell Mark, a tiny choked cry of distress escaped her.

'Susannah?'

Mark jerked upright, golden eyes searching her face, and even though she closed her lids against the intensity of his scrutiny, fearful of how he might interpret her distress, he caught the glimmer of a tear on her dark lashes and she felt his long body stiffen in suspicion.

'Susannah?' he said on a new and very dangerous note. 'What is it?'

There was no way she could lie. He would know if she did.

'Simon...'

The name was just a whisper, but he caught it, and she felt the bed move violently as he flung himself to his feet. Too afraid to open her eyes, Susannah lay as if frozen, hearing the rustle of material and praying that it was not what she feared. But then, at the unmistakable sound of a zip being fastened roughly, she knew she could no longer hope and her eyes flew open and she sat up hastily to see that he was fully dressed and heading for the door.

'Mark?' she began fearfully, thinking at first that he hadn't heard her because it wasn't until the handle was actually in his grasp that he half turned and flung a scowling glance at her over his shoulder. 'Where—where are you going?'

'Out.' The single syllable was flung at her with cold contempt, his expression implacable.

'But why——?'

Her voice failed, drying painfully in the incandescent heat of the fury in his eyes. She knew why, of course she did. In the moment that she had spoken Simon's name she had destroyed everything that had been between them once and for all.

'I'm sorry,' she whispered, knowing it was too late.

'Why the hell did you come here?'

The truth was that she'd almost forgotten. It took a couple of seconds' thought to remember Andi's excitement about the contracts.

'Andi...'

'Ah, yes—you wanted to make sure that my signature really was going on that precious piece of paper.'

Mark's tone frightened her. She felt that its cold savagery might actually slash at her vulnerable nerves.

'You wouldn't...'

If the way he spoke had been worrying, his laughter appalled her.

'Oh, no, sweetheart, you've nothing to fear on that score. I gave Theo my word and I won't go back on it. But let me tell you something——' His voice changed, took on a disturbingly intimate, confiding note. 'That contract was never in any danger, right from the start.'

'But you said——'

'Oh, no, darling——' the endearment was laced with burning acid '—*you* were the one who brought the word blackmail into the conversation. You handed me the idea on a plate—I'd have been a fool not to use it.'

Susannah couldn't believe what she was hearing. He had been playing with her all along, manipulating her into doing just what he wanted like some depraved puppet master pulling her strings.

'So you see, Calypso, you made the ultimate sacrifice—betrayed the memory of your precious Simon—all for nothing.'

'It wasn't like that——' Susannah began, but Mark ignored her.

'I'd be grateful if you weren't here when I got back,' he continued in that clipped curt voice as if she hadn't spoken. 'I couldn't be answerable for my reactions if you were.'

'But, Mark——'

But she was speaking to empty air. He had gone as soon as he had finished speaking, and as the door slammed shut behind him Susannah sank back on the bed, burying her face in the pillow which still bore the imprint of his head, the scent of his body. Hot, bitter tears burned in her eyes like acid, sliding from under her lids and soaking into the crisp white cotton, and the desolation in her heart was like a savage wound as she realised that she was no longer weeping for Simon but for the fact that Mark would never know that the other man could never, ever be the rival he imagined him to be.

CHAPTER ELEVEN

'OH, WHERE are they?'

For perhaps the tenth time in the past half-hour, Susannah stood up, looking around her anxiously, peering over the heads of the people surrounding her, searching for her sister's face.

'They're going to be late!'

'If they can make it, they will.' Mark sounded totally indifferent to her concern.

'But they'll miss everything if they don't get here soon—and they'll never find us in this crush!'

'Susannah, sit down!' Impatience put a harsh edge on Mark's voice. 'You know what Jamie's like when he won't settle——'

'Oh, but——'

'Sit down!'

Brusque and rough, his tone had her lowering herself to her seat in an ungainly rush. Mark made no comment on her obedient response to his command, his face coldly distant. A moment later he pushed one hand through the tawny softness of his hair and Susannah felt her nerves twist in instinctive response to the way the glory of the setting sun caught on it, gleaming fiercely.

'I appreciate that you have no desire to be in my company.' The words might have come from a tongue that was made of wood, they sounded so stiff and hard. 'But I promised Andi you'd see the procession, and I intend to keep my word, so——'

'But——'

Susannah bit her words off sharply, not really knowing what to say. Since the night in his bedroom, Mark seemed to have reverted to the meticulous politeness he had shown her during her first days on the island, but this time there was something so very different about his attitude.

157

At the beginning, he had seemed almost to be amused by their careful performances, a gleam of amusement almost permanently warming the golden eyes, a tiny smile curling the corners of his mouth. Now he was as hard and unyielding as the giant limestone slabs that made up the temples at Ggantija. It was as if he had erected huge barriers around himself, all of them plastered with signs declaring 'Keep Out!' and 'Trespassers will be prosecuted', and even if Susannah had been tempted to try to break down the defences he had built against her, then the way that he made sure that they were never alone, the icy coldness that emanated from him, freezing her right to her heart, left her unable to open her mouth to say a single word.

The contracts had been signed, and that at least should have given her a sense of release, but what she felt was in fact the exact opposite. The night in Mark's bedroom constantly came back to haunt her, making her feel so ill at ease in his presence that she would never have been with him tonight, no matter how much she wanted to see the Good Friday procession, if Andrea and Theo hadn't said that they would be coming too. But at the last minute baby James had refused to settle with his paternal grandmother, and his parents had stayed behind, urging Mark and Susannah to go on ahead, they would join them later.

'The procession will start from the church——' Mark was carefully turning the conversation on to safer, unprovocative paths '—and make its way through the village.'

He touched her arm gently in order to draw her attention to the route.

'Yes—I see . . .'

Susannah was amazed that she could manage to form any response at all. Just the light touch of his hand on her arm was enough to send quivers of reaction running through her, awakening painful echoes of the way he had made her feel just two nights before. Her heart started thudding violently, shivers sliding down her spine. She was so intensely physically aware of him sitting beside her in a black T-shirt and jeans, a lightweight grey and black check jacket slung loosely around his shoulders, that she found it difficult to breathe naturally, convinced that he must hear the pounding of her heart even through the funereal music that was pouring from the loudspeakers placed among the trees.

'Are you cold?' Mark had caught her shudder of response.

'No—I'm fine...' Hot colour washed her cheeks with the recollection of just what those words had led to in the past. 'Andi warned me that it could get quite cool when the sun went down so I came prepared...'

With a hand that wasn't quite steady, she indicated the turquoise knitted cotton cardigan knotted around her waist, then immediately wished she hadn't as she saw those amber eyes drop down to survey her slim hips and the amount of long, golden-toned leg exposed by the white shorts she wore with a short-sleeved top that matched the cardigan. Swallowing hard to ease a suddenly dry throat, she tried desperately to think of something to say to distract him, but at that moment the pounding of drums sounded to her left, drawing her attention.

'It's starting!'

Craning her neck to see over the heads of the crowd, she caught a glimpse of red and white plumes and the glint of gold as villagers dressed in the costumes of Roman soldiers made their way slowly down the main street from the church.

'Oh!' It was a cry of delight and surprise. She had expected the sort of amateurish, hastily put together costumes of a school nativity play—nothing this spectacular.

'The costumes are made by the villagers themselves,' Mark said quietly. 'They take great pride in them. Some are perhaps fifty years old or more, but they're very carefully looked after. It's regarded as a great honour to be in the procession, and the wealthy members of the community sponsor the statues that are carried——'

'Look!'

Susannah was unaware of having broken in on him, her hand reaching out unconsciously to touch his arm as she gazed at the white-robed figures, their hair covered by white head-dresses, who came slowly down the street,

bearing on their shoulders a life-sized model of Christ
and an angel, the whole thing surrounded by dozens of
lighted candles.

'When you said statues, I thought you meant little
ones—that must weigh a ton!'

'Close to it.' Mark nodded. 'Even though they're made
out of painted papier mâché. It takes ten or more men
to carry each one, and they need frequent rests—that's
why the procession moves so slowly. Each tableau re-
presents one of the Stations of the Cross, and there are
about fourteen in all—this one's the Garden of
Gethsemane, and the next is Jesus before Pilate...'

For a time Susannah watched in absorbed fascination
as the procession made its slow, stately way past them,
Mark explaining each different tableau as it appeared.
She barely noticed that the sun had gone down completely, the gathering dusk highlighting the dramatic
effect of the many candles, until suddenly the atmosphere changed, and a group of men dressed in white and
wearing chains and carrying full-sized crosses appeared.
Seeing the eerie white hoods which covered their faces
except for holes cut for their eyes, Susannah shivered
involuntarily.

'Who—what are they?' she asked, unable to control
the faint quaver in her voice.

'*Penitentes*,' Mark answered. 'Traditionally they are
supposed to be doing penance for some sin—no one is
supposed to know who's behind the mask. I think it's
time you put your cardigan on,' he added, as Susannah
gave another uncontrollable shiver. 'Here—let me...'

He was right, it had become decidedly cool, Susannah
realised with a sense of shock, shivering in earnest now
as he helped her into the turquoise cardigan. The sombre,
rather frightening spectacle of the penitents still lingered
so that when Mark, seeing her disturbed expression,
moved closer and slung an arm around her shoulders,
it seemed right and surprisingly easy to respond to the
casual gesture by moving closer into the warmth of his
body, letting it melt some of the ice around her heart as
well as easing her physical discomfort.

'Better now?' he asked after a few moments, and
Susannah could only nod silently, the overwhelming

sense of rightness, of completeness she was experiencing closing her throat and depriving her of the ability to speak. 'I'm not surprised you're feeling chilled—we've been here for over two hours—it's almost seven. Are you hungry?'

To her surprise, Susannah found that she was. After all, she had last eaten anything at lunchtime, and then, her appetite muted by her discomfort at being seated directly opposite Mark, she had only managed to force down a very small amount. Now however she found that her stomach felt uncomfortably empty.

'Starving,' she admitted frankly, glad to find that her voice functioned after all, even sounding surprisingly confident. 'But——'

'Hang on...'

Mark paused for a second to shrug himself out of his jacket and drape it around her shoulders before he left her side, pushing through the crowd towards the edge of the street. Watching him, Susannah saw him make his way towards a small, brightly lit snack bar.

He must be cold without his jacket, she thought, pulling it more tightly round her; she was still not comfortable even with both it and her cardigan. But the real reason for the way she was feeling, she realised a moment later, was that without the warmth and comforting strength of Mark's body beside her she felt lost and miserably bereft in a way that was emotional rather than physical.

Another convulsive shiver shook her slender body, one that had nothing to do with the cool of the evening, and she pulled the jacket close around her, drawing an intense comfort from the fact that the fine material still retained some of Mark's warmth and the tang of his aftershave, together with the more subtle, personal scent that was his alone. She wished he would hurry back. It was crazy; he had only been gone a few moments and yet she missed him desperately.

When she realised just what she was feeling, Susannah's thought processes suddenly stopped dead, leaving her staring blankly into space, her unfocused eyes not even registering the spectacle of the procession before her. How could she feel like this about this man—a man

who had made it plain that the only appeal she had for
him was purely physical, who had declared quite openly
his selfish intention of ignoring her needs and wishes
and feeding only his own sexual desires—as he had done
only two nights ago?

But then, wouldn't she be lying if she said that the
time they had made love had been against her wishes?
A ruthless conscience made her face the facts, forcing
her to admit that she had been a willing partner—willing
and eager. There had been no forced seduction, no undue
pressure, no move that she hadn't welcomed as she had
done on every occasion the previous year. What was it
about Mark that could make her behave in this way,
contradicting every principle by which she had formerly
lived her life?

Her thoughts went back to a conversation she had had
with Andrea in the early hours of that morning. Unable
to sleep, she had heard Jamie's hungry cry and her sister
getting up to go to him. As she was awake anyway, she
had decided to see if she could be of any help and so
had joined them in the nursery. Perhaps it had been the
lateness of the hour and the fact that, in the darkness
of the night, everyone else was asleep that had loosened
her tongue, she didn't know, but the end result was that
she had poured everything out, confiding the whole sorry
story of her conflict with Mark to her sister's sympathetic ears.

Andrea had listened in silence, making no comment,
until Susannah had finally paused for breath, and then
she had leaned forward, her expression thoughtful.

'Did you feel like this all the time you were with
Mark?' she asked. 'Or was it just later?'

Susannah had frowned her incomprehension. 'What
do you mean? I don't understand.'

'Did you feel so—wrong—so guilty about the way
Mark made you act and feel when you were with him
last year?'

'No—I felt——' Susannah hesitated. 'At first it felt
so *good*.'

There had been no sense of right or wrong then; it
had all been so perfect, so natural, like a dream from
which she never wanted to waken—an idyllic bubble

suspended out of time. But it couldn't stay that way; inevitably, reality had intruded.

'Then it was only when you thought of Simon—after you got that phone call—that you felt bad?'

'No—Simon and I were over. I felt guilty because I went against what I believed in. I compromised my principles for a holiday fling——'

Seeing her sister's sceptical expression, she had stopped abruptly, forced to reconsider. She had to admit that during the time she had spent with Mark no sense of guilt had ever intruded; it *had* only been when she had received that terrible phone call from her father that she had been forced to remember Simon—because the truth was that up until that moment she had *forgotten* about him, his memory burned away in the incandescent heat of the flames of passion that Mark's lovemaking awoke in her.

'I'm right.' Andrea had seen her change of expression.

'No...' But Susannah's response no longer had her earlier confident conviction. She had spoken the truth when she had said that she and Simon were finished. She had never spared him a thought until the phone call—when she had learned that, while she had been revelling in the sensual, hedonistic pleasures of her irresponsible idyll, Simon had——

'Here—this should make you feel better.'

Mark's voice broke into Susannah's thoughts, jolting her violently back to the present so that she jumped like a startled cat.

'Hey—I didn't mean to frighten you.' Mark's tone was husky with genuine concern, something that, in her present vulnerable and disturbed state of mind, was like a soothing balm to her jagged nerves, a welcome relief after the cold, hard-edged tones he had used before, bringing hot tears to her eyes.

'I—I'm sorry...' Hastily she blinked them back, determined not to let him see her weakness. 'I was miles away.'

She could only pray that Mark would attribute the wobble in her voice to the shock of his sudden appearance but the truth was that his nearness, his strong body so close that she could feel its warmth reaching

her, was tying her insides into knots. An intense
awareness of his height, the imposing width of his
shoulders, the narrow waist, lean hips and long, long
legs in the tight-fitting jeans made her heart leap and
start to thud heavily, its beat so strong that she was sure
he must hear its thunderous pounding, see the disturbing effect it was having on her breathing.

With an effort she focused on the brown paper bag
he held. 'What's this?'

'Something to ease the hunger pangs—hot *pastizzi*—
cheese pastries—try one.'

Susannah needed no further encouragement, her eyes
rounding in delight as she bit into the crisp flaky pastry.

'Oh, that's delicious!' she managed, when her mouth
was empty.

'Good, aren't they?' Mark laughed down at her blissful
expression, his own face warming in response to her obvious enjoyment. 'They're made with ricotta cheese—
and those others are pea and onion. Go on, have
another.'

But Susannah barely heard his warm-voiced encouragement. In the moment that he had smiled at her, it
had been as if the village street with its lights and music,
the crowds and the colour and spectacle of the procession still continuing in the background, had all faded,
becoming just a blur at the edge of her awareness. Her
breath seemed to lock in her lungs, and she could neither
let it out nor draw any more in to ease the intolerable
tension in her chest. All she was aware of was the physical
presence of this man beside her, the lean strength of his
body, the sound of his voice, and the warmth of those
golden eyes which now seemed so deep that she felt she
was being drawn into them, drifting, floating away on
a glowing sea of feeling.

Andrea had been right; she had put her finger unerr-
ingly on the truth of the matter, on the flaw in her own
reasoning. She had been looking at things back to front
all the time.

'I hate him!' she had declared, but, as her sister had
often teased her, in her anger she had spoken the opposite of the true way she was feeling. Her head reeling
as if from the force of a powerful blow, Susannah shakily

began to focus her hazy mind on a totally new interpretation of the facts, one that turned everything upside down.

She didn't hate Mark, she *loved* him—becoming aware for the first time what love in its fullest force really meant. This was the feeling that had changed her sister's life so completely, taking her off to another country to live in order to be with the man she loved. This shattering, explosive sensation of not knowing whether you were on your head or your heels, of being in a world in which all your earlier beliefs and values no longer existed—a world that had absorbed her so completely that she had been incapable of thinking straight, of considering anything rationally—she had only been able to *feel*.

But because she hadn't known what had hit her, because she had always been the sensible one, the one who thought things through logically, the one who was never impulsive, never emotional, she hadn't recognised the feeling for what it was.

'Susannah?'

Mark's tone was questioning, a frown creasing his forehead. He was going to ask her what was wrong, she thought frantically, and there was no way she could possibly answer him.

She knew now how *she* felt, but what about Mark? It seemed as if every nerve in her body had come tinglingly alive, and where before she had felt chilled, now her racing blood heated her skin so that she was glad of the evening shadows which hid the fiery colour in her cheeks. Her heart was beating so frantically that she felt it might almost burst out of her chest, her ribcage seeming too fragile to contain its powerful throbbing, and her inner tension, the yearning awareness that gripped her was so strong that she felt sure he must feel it as something almost tangible, something actually shimmering between them. He had felt something like it on Wednesday night—but that had been before she had so foolishly destroyed the mood—and now that he had had what he wanted of her, would he ever feel it again?

'Susannah!'

'I'm sorry—I don't—I...'

As Susannah struggled to find some response, her eyes were drawn once more to the street where the procession was now nearing its end. Just as she focused on it once more, the bearers of the last tableau halted directly in front of her. Confronted by the gruesome image of Christ placed in the tomb, she drew in her breath in a gasping cry of shock. The figure was so appallingly real-looking, frighteningly so, the sight of it forcing to the surface of her mind the final, terrible memory that she had tried so hard to bury.

'Susannah!' Mark said again, concern sharpening his tone. 'What is it?'

'Simon...'

Her face deathly white, she reached out a shaking hand and felt it taken in a warm, comforting grasp.

'Tell me!' he commanded, his voice husky and rough. 'Susannah, tell me what is wrong!' he repeated, giving her a little shake as Susannah's dark, shocked blue eyes swung once again to the macabre statue.

'Simon...'

The words seemed to stick in her throat, needing to be said, but impossible to force out past the tight, painful knot that had formed there.

'Simon—he—died.'

'*What*?'

For a second there was a stunned, shocked silence, Mark's face growing almost as pale as her own. But then, looking into her eyes, he saw their bruised look, the glisten of unshed tears.

'Oh, God—Susannah!'

Strong arms came round her, supporting her as she leaned against them faintly, and he guided her carefully through the crush of people, away from the route of the procession.

'Come on, Calypso—we're getting out of here.'

CHAPTER TWELVE

'Do you feel ready to talk yet?'

Mark didn't look at Susannah as he spoke, his eyes fixed on a point far beyond the windscreen of the car, watching the small, moonlit waves lap against the pebbled shore of the rocky cove where they had finally stopped.

'About Simon, I mean,' he added when she didn't respond, and Susannah felt a touch of slightly bitter laughter shake her body.

Oh, yes, she was ready to talk about Simon now. She could talk about the *past* without difficulty—it was the present, and, even more so, the future that gave her problems. But Mark was waiting for her to say something, and she supposed that Simon was as good a point to start as any.

'Simon and I...' she began softly, then stopped, her heart clenching painfully as he turned his dark head towards her and she saw how his golden eyes gleamed in the clear moonlight.

I love you! The words burned on her tongue, the need to speak them sharp as a pain. But she couldn't say them. There was too much unfinished business between them, and even if the past was put behind them she still didn't know if there was any possibility of a future. After all, Mark had never spoken a single word of love. He had never talked of wanting anything other than the passionate sexual relationship which he had made plain was uppermost in his thoughts and to which end he had deliberately used every manipulative skill he possessed, particularly the weapon which she unknowingly had handed him. But even as Susannah faced up to that fact, she knew, deep down, that if a sexual affair was all that Mark offered, then she would accept it. But first she had to clear the air about Simon.

'I told you that everyone thought we would marry.'

Her voice had a new strength, gained from the conviction that this had to be said if there was ever to be any hope of a relationship between them.

'According to my parents, Simon was perfect husband material—steady, reliable—he had a good job.' Her voice shook slightly. 'The job I have now.'

'Take it easy,' Mark said when she hesitated, his soft voice gently encouraging. 'There's no rush—we have all night.'

All night to talk, Susannah reflected sadly—but after that—then what? It wasn't easy to think straight with Mark sitting stiffly and silently beside her. The dark confines of the car seemed smaller than ever before, constrictingly claustrophobic, and every tiny inch of her body was hypersensitive to each breath he drew, any movement of his lean, strong body.

'It seemed our future was mapped out, but then, when Simon proposed, I realised that we'd been too close to each other—going out together, working together. I'd never really been able to see him properly, just what other people saw in him—what everyone else expected. Somehow when he asked me to marry him it was as if he came back into focus and I knew I couldn't say yes. He...'

Bitter tears of memory burned at her eyes and she blinked furiously to drive them back.

'He took it badly.' Mark's tone was as flat as her thoughts.

'Yes.' Susannah shivered at the thought of just how badly. 'He wouldn't take no for an answer. He followed me everywhere—rang up at all hours of the day and night, sat outside my flat in his car. He was convinced that if he asked me often enough then eventually I'd give in.' Drawing a deep breath, she gathered the strength to go on. 'When I didn't, he threatened to kill himself——' Startled by Mark's savage expletive, she turned towards him sharply, seeing how tightly drawn his face was, the skin stretched tight over the high cheekbones.

'Oh, no,' she said hastily, reading his thoughts. 'That wasn't how—he didn't—it was to get away from the pressure he was putting on me that I came here—and then I met you.'

And because she had been trying to escape from a relationship that had gone sour, because she had been convinced that the last thing she was looking for was love, she hadn't been able to recognise it when it exploded in her face. Believing, like Simon, like her parents, that love grew steadily and slowly from a long-term relationship, she had been shocked to discover that what she felt for Simon wasn't *enough*. Running from his distorted idea of love, she had tumbled headlong into an affair with Mark, believing that the free and casual relationship he offered was what she needed. But it hadn't been just that; Mark had made her feel very special, and her damaged self-esteem had needed that too.

'And, being ripe for an affair, you fell into my arms.'

Susannah winced at the bitterness in Mark's voice, unable to deny that that was how it must seem to him. After all, hadn't she once thought that way herself? It was only one brief hour since she had realised the real truth, and she hadn't yet come to terms with it. But did the anger that Mark showed mean that he too had felt more than she had ever imagined? She didn't know and didn't dare to ask, knowing that a negative answer would destroy her.

'I thought that something light-hearted—no commitment...' She couldn't go on. That was how she had felt at the time; now it was no longer true.

There was a difficult silence as Mark absorbed her hesitant words, a taut, somehow dangerous silence that stretched Susannah's nerves almost to breaking point, her need for him to say something warring with her fear of just what he might say if he did. When he finally spoke, his words were so unexpected that she was not sure if she had heard him right.

'You and Simon weren't lovers.' It was a statement of fact, not a question.

'We...'

'You never slept with him.' The flatness of Mark's tone betrayed nothing of his feelings, and even in the

moonlight it was impossible to read his expression, his
eyes just dark, impenetrable pools.

'N—no—we both believed in waiting—in commitment.'

And yet with Mark she hadn't held back. After just
a few short hours in his company—barely a full day—
she had leapt into his bed. Not believing in love at first
sight, she hadn't recognised what was happening to her.

'Then why me?' Mark demanded harshly.

How did she answer that? Twice Susannah opened
her mouth to tell him the truth, but both times her voice
failed her completely.

'You—you were there...' she managed at last, wanting
to add *and I loved you*, but her tongue seemed incapable
of forming the words. But she had to add *something*;
left like that, it was far too stark, too unfeeling——

'And any man would do,' Mark finished for her, and
she winced at the black cynicism of his tone.

'No!' she cried sharply, but too late. He had already
flung himself out of the car and was standing, hands
thrust deep into his pockets, shoulders hunched, staring
moodily out at the sea.

In desperate haste, Susannah scrambled out of her seat
and into the cool night air.

'*No!*' she repeated, the forcefulness of her declaration
bringing his head round sharply so that they faced each
other over the top of the car. 'You weren't just any man.
I'd never met anyone who could make me feel that way
before.'

From the way his mouth twisted she knew she hadn't
said enough. She regretted the way she had made it sound
purely physical, but she didn't dare to add any more.

'Simon couldn't make you feel like that.'

A dark satisfaction sounded in Mark's voice and
Susannah's heart twisted painfully, something like the
bitter bite of acid burning savagely at the thought that
this was what affected him most—the feeling of sexual
triumph, of knowing that she responded to him as she
had never responded to anyone else, not even the man
with whom she had spent almost two years. Mark was
almost gloating over the fact that *he* had been able to

awaken the sensuality inside her which no one else had been able to reach.

With a terrible sense of despair, Susannah knew that this was why she had been afraid of seeing him again. Deep down, on some subconscious level, never rationally acknowledged, she had known that she had fallen for Mark in a way that she had never known before. She had explained her refusal to marry Simon by saying that the special spark wasn't there—but now she knew love wasn't like that. With Mark it hadn't been a spark but a conflagration that had burned up all considerations of principle or common sense. It was a spell, an enchantment, like the one that had possessed Ulysses, holding him captive on the island for seven years. Love wasn't sensible or logical; it had swept through her life like a whirlwind, turning everything upside down.

And so, even though she hadn't known what had hit her, she had been afraid of meeting Mark again, afraid of the cataclysmic effect he could have on her. She had been afraid of facing the way she really felt about him, and—even worse—facing the possibility that he might not love her in return.

'So what happened?' Mark's voice sounded calm and even, but the distant, unapproachable look was back in his eyes. 'To Simon,' he prompted when she hesitated, unable for the moment to recall what they had been talking about.

'He—took a group of teenagers on a climbing expedition. There was an accident——' It took a terrible effort to go on. 'He fell and was very badly hurt...'

In the midst of her misery, she became aware of the way that Mark had reached across the roof of the car to take her hand, the warm touch of his fingers giving her the strength she needed.

'That was what the phone call was about—I *had* to go!'

She willed him to understand and knew from the way his fingers tightened on her hand that he did.

'He—he died an hour before I reached the hospital. I couldn't even say goodbye and tell him I was sorry...'

Mark's hard fingers moved on hers. 'Sorry—for what?'

'For not loving him the way he wanted.' Susannah's voice was bleak. 'I was afraid that it was my fault—that he had done it deliberately.'

There, it was said at last. For the first time she had managed to voice her worst fears.

Once more Mark's savage curse slashed through the silence of the night, and he released her hand abruptly, moving swiftly round the car to take her in his arms.

'Susannah, *no*! You mustn't think that! You said yourself it was an accident.'

'But he loved me so much!'

Mark's face darkened, his eyes cold and hard.

'That isn't love—it's obsession—wanting to own the other person, possess them so completely...'

His expression changed suddenly, looking strangely bleak, desolate somehow.

'That's how Calypso held Ulysses, keeping him prisoner.'

And Mark had called her Calypso. Was that how he saw the passion he felt for her? As an imprisonment from which he wanted to break free?

'I just wish he'd known that I cared.' After all, she had loved him in a way; not as she now knew she loved Mark, but she had been very fond of Simon.

'He did!' Mark looked deep into her eyes, gripping her arms tightly as if trying to communicate the certainty he felt through touch. 'He would have known——'

'Yes—he would.'

Susannah felt the force of his conviction fill her like a flood of heat through her body, easing the ache she had carried with her for so long. It had overshadowed her relationship with Mark, she now realised, distorting and discolouring her feelings.

'And you're right—he didn't really love me...'

She could see that now because she knew what love was really like; how it became part of life, essential as the air you breathed, so that everything was brighter and better because the person you loved was in the world. And real love also meant that you cared enough to accept that, if the other person didn't love you, you couldn't hold them—you had to give them their freedom, stand back and watch them walk away. That was what Simon hadn't been able to do for her, but the most difficult, most painful question of all was, would she have to do it for Mark?

She had never been so intensely physically aware of him as in that moment, every cell in her body burning in response to the warmth and strength of his lean frame so close to her, the power of his arms around her, his face so close to hers. She loved him with a depth that frightened her, and she couldn't go on without knowing how he felt about her.

'Have you ever loved anyone, Mark?' she asked impetuously, and saw his head go back, those golden eyes eerily drained of all colour in the moonlight, making her think worryingly of a hunting animal's.

'Love?' he echoed as if he hadn't understood the word. 'Don't ask me. How the hell should I know what love is, anyway? It's just a fantasy...'

He shook his head almost violently, releasing her and turning away.

'I don't know...' he said again, a strange note, one that Susannah couldn't begin to interpret, shading his voice.

Susannah's heart seemed to have plummeted to somewhere beneath the soles of her feet. She had given him an opportunity, had tried in a not very subtle way to get him to open up—to admit to his feelings, if he had any. If he had given her such a chance, she knew she couldn't have held back; she would have had to pour out everything about the way she felt about him. But Mark, it seemed, had nothing to say.

But hadn't she already faced that possibility? Hadn't she acknowledged to herself that if he didn't feel anything else for her she would be satisfied with the sexual passion which he had always shown her? Perhaps, in time, it could grow into something more. Or was she being all sorts of a fool, deceiving herself with blind, crazy hope? She couldn't answer that, only knew that she couldn't bear to see him turn away from her like that. She had to keep him with her, and would accept however little he chose to give her, like a starving person, grateful for a few crusts from a rich man's table.

'Mark...'

Reaching out impulsively, she caught hold of his arm, loving the feel of his warm skin, the strength of muscle and bone, her heart lurching into a rapid, uneven pattern. Her resolve faltered when he turned back and she saw the withdrawn, coldly distant expression that made his face seem to be carved from marble, all colour drained from his skin in the moonlight.

'I—thank you...' she managed, though her throat was dry and tight, making it difficult to speak.

'I'm glad I was here for you.' He sounded like someone who had learned his lines by rote, but was incapable of injecting any emotion into them. 'You were tangled up in your feelings and needed some help breaking free from them.'

Was that all he thought it had been? Did he really believe her capable of simply using him in that way—as a release from the frustration and tension that had built up inside her as a result of Simon's behaviour and an escape from her sense of fear and guilt? She couldn't bear the thought—and she couldn't cope with his distant mood any longer.

'Mark!' she murmured, softly reproving, sliding her arms around his narrow waist and drawing him closer. 'Don't be like this! I want to thank you properly—I...'

The tormenting emotions swirling in her mind finally overwhelmed her, pushing her into rash, unconsidered speech.

'Kiss me!' she half begged, half commanded, not caring whether she was being crazy, if her words were downright dangerous.

For a long, painful moment, she thought he hadn't heard her, or, if he had, that he wasn't going to respond, but then suddenly, swiftly, as if he too was overcome by the way he felt, his dark head lowered, his lips covering hers in a violent, greedily snatching kiss, one that came closer to assault than a caress. Despairingly, Susannah was a prey to the terrible thought that this was all he wanted, that he would take this one harsh, punishing kiss and then leave her. But then, in the moment that his mouth touched hers, something changed, softening his reaction, making the kiss he gave her more gentle,

more sensuous, drawing a response from her that made
the stars in the night sky spin around her head.

With a deep, contented sigh she moved closer, pressing
her body against his, feeling the blood heat in her veins
as her hungry fingers caressed the hard strength of his
neck, the tight muscles of his back and shoulders,
smoothing down over the strong ribcage towards the slim
waist. Her mouth softened and opened under his, welcoming the intimate invasion of his tongue, making her
writhe in delight, the burning need she had been desperately holding in check uncoiling deep in the pit of
her stomach, filling her body with an aching yearning
that was almost more than she could bear.

'Mark!' His name was a whisper of longing that escaped when at last her lips were freed as Mark drew in
a deep, uneven breath. 'You know how I want you—
how I——'

How I love you, she would have said, but before she
could finish the sentence he had cursed savagely,
wrenching himself away from her once more, the rough
movement tearing at her heart as he caught her caressing
hands and forced them down to her sides.

'No!' It was a raw, ragged sound, his breathing harsh
and rough.

'No?' Susannah couldn't believe what she was hearing.
'But, Mark...'

Past thinking, past caring what she revealed about her
feelings for him, she moved to press another kiss against
his mouth, pain stabbing deep into her heart as he repulsed the gesture with a brusque movement of his head,
her lips landing awkwardly on the hard, unyielding plane
of his cheek.

'I said *no*!'

The cold finality of his tone drained all hope from
her, one hand going shakily to her bruised lips, her eyes
wide, dark pools of shock above ashen cheeks.

'It won't work,' Mark declared brutally, his words
seeming to slash into her sensitised flesh like cruelly sharp
knives. 'We can't go back...'

'But what we had——' Susannah protested.

'Isn't there any more,' he returned implacably, every syllable falling like a blow on her bruised heart. 'It won't work,' he repeated. 'It's over——'

And as she watched him stride away from her, pulling open the car door and flinging himself into the driving seat, she knew she had lost him. The violent slam of the door closing against her was clearer evidence of the finality of his decision than any words he might say. Susannah knew that no argument, no attempt at persuasion, no pleading, could bring him to change his mind. Her heart seemed to shrivel and die inside her as she recalled how, less than a week before, Mark had told her that their affair would be over only when he said it was.

Now it seemed that that time had come, and all she could do was try to find the strength to accept that fact. She would have been prepared to settle for only physical passion if that had been all that Mark had to offer her, no longer daring to hope for love, but now it seemed that even that had died. She had sensed the truth in his brutal response to her kiss just a few bitter moments ago, knowing that it spelt the end of all her hopes, her short-lived dreams.

Not only did Mark not love her—he had said he didn't know what love was, describing it as just a fantasy—but he didn't even want her physically any more, which meant that he had nothing at all to give her. In his mind, their relationship was finally and completely over and it was the bitterest irony of all that he should come to that decision now, when she was prepared to give him anything—everything—he wanted if he would only ask.

But he would never ask; and it seemed that the only thing he wanted from her was that she would leave him alone. It cut her to the heart, the pain searing through her in white-hot agony, but she would never show him how much he had hurt her. If the only way she could show her love was by letting him go, then she would do it, accepting her dismissal with as much dignity and strength as she could muster.

CHAPTER THIRTEEN

SUSANNAH placed her posy of flowers on Simon's grave and ran her fingers lightly over the carved letters of his name, a small, sad smile on her lips. She would always remember her friend with affection, the dreadful feeling of fear and guilt no longer a problem. Now she could recall all the good times they had had together and not the terrible way the relationship had ended.

If only she could feel that way about Mark too—but that was impossible. Susannah doubted if it would ever be possible to erase the pain she felt at just thinking of him. It was a struggle simply to get through each day, but the nights were the worst. When the darkness came, and with it all the bitter memories, she felt she would break in two from the hurt of losing him.

'Calypso...'

The voice was so soft, almost a whisper, that for a moment she thought that she had imagined it, heard it only inside her head, the sound of those beloved tones conjured up by her own private longings.

But then, 'Susannah,' it said again, and at the corner of her eye a small movement alerted her, making her look around sharply.

'Mark!'

It couldn't be! She was dreaming—the heartbreakingly familiar tall, strong figure with the gleaming bronze hair just a figment of her imagination. But then he smiled and stepped forward, holding out his hand to help her to her feet.

'Your mother said I'd find you here.'

'Oh—yes...'

It was hard to speak naturally when her heart was racing crazily, beating against her ribs like the desperate wings of a trapped bird.

'I like to bring flowers—after all, we were—friends.'

Mark nodded silently, still holding her hand, and, weak as she was, she let her fingers lie in his, not daring to move and alert him to their position for fear he would immediately let go again. Hungrily she took in his appearance, only fully realising now, when she saw him in the flesh at last, how much she had missed him and how inadequate her imaginings and dreams had been, the six weeks since she had returned from Malta stretching out like a barren desert of time.

He looked tired, she thought with some concern, those golden eyes dimmed by the shadows in and around them. The tan he had acquired on the island had faded, making him look pale and drawn, and he appeared to have lost weight, the ancient jeans he wore with an equally battered denim jacket looking loose around his narrow waist and hips.

'Can I walk you back home?' he asked, and at the sound of the strangely diffident, almost hesitant, note in his voice Susannah couldn't help wondering if she was hearing things. The Mark she had known would have taken what he wanted, not asked.

But then, she reflected unhappily, she didn't really know Mark any more. Once the passionate, blazing sexual affair between them had ended, there had been no time to renegotiate the situation, develop a new way of communicating with each other. During the forty-eight hours which were all that Mark had spent on the island after the Good Friday procession, he had reverted to the immaculately polite behaviour that he had used before and that, feeling as she did, had been as effective at distancing him from her as if he had actually put up physical barriers between them. Loving him as she did, it was sheer misery to be treated like some total stranger, not even meriting the light-hearted warmth he showed Andrea.

'Of course...'

Susannah fully expected that now he would release his grip on her hand, but he still seemed to be unaware of it, and, greedy for even the slightest contact with him, she made no move to draw away, struggling to control the excited response of her body to his touch, her heart pounding heavily, the warmth of his palm against hers

both a source of intense pleasure and bitter pain at the
thought that it was so fleeting a delight.

'Are you working near here—or do you have friends
in the area that you're visiting?' she asked when they
had left the graveyard and were walking back towards
the town.

'Neither...'

Those amber eyes met hers in a long, disturbingly
intent look, one that made her heart feel as if it had
suddenly stopped beating then jerked back into violent
action once more.

'I came to see you. Andi gave me your address. She
wasn't too sure if she should at first, but——' a grin,
lop-sided and boyishly wry, surfaced suddenly '—I
managed to persuade her.'

Andrea would have been putty in his hands if he'd
turned that charm on her, Susannah reflected, torn between cursing her sister for letting him know where she
could be found and being deeply thankful that she had.
During the past six weeks, she had reached a form of
peace—an ability, if not to accept, then at least to be
able to live with the loss of the man she loved so desperately. Now it would all have to be done again, and
yet—seeing him here with her now, for however short a
time—she couldn't wish it otherwise in spite of the inevitable pain when he left. She could only drink in the
sight of him, his smile, the sound of his voice, like a
starving person suddenly offered a feast at which to gorge
herself—for a very strictly limited time.

'She gave me your parents' address too. So when I
called at your flat and you were out, I went there—I'd
already been to the leisure centre.'

He'd been determined to find her, Susannah thought,
her heart skipping another beat—which led inevitably
to the question, why? What was it that he wanted?

'It's my day off.'

It was all that she could manage, the struggle to suppress the tiny, irrational voice that spoke of a crazy hope
that he had come looking for her because he had missed
her occupying her mind. She was only fooling herself to
even consider the possibility. During those last two days
on the island, he had given no indication of any feeling

other than total indifference, the blazing desire he had once shown having burned itself out so completely that all that was left was rapidly cooling ash.

'Did I leave something behind—at the hotel?'

It was the only possibility she could think of, that perhaps she had dropped something in his room. Her mind flinched away from recalling the time she had spent there—the passion that had flared between them for the last time.

'No.' The single syllable was curt and hard.

'Then what——?'

'Look, Susannah—do you mind if we leave it till we get inside? I'd rather talk about this in private.'

Which, of course, was guaranteed to worry her even more, her tension growing by the second as they completed the short journey to the house in which she had the ground floor flat. By the time they got there, Susannah was in such a state that her hand shook betrayingly as she tried to insert the key in the lock and she had to pull away from Mark and use her other hand to hold it firmly. She waited only until they were in her small, comfortable living-room before she turned to Mark.

'What is it?' she asked in a rush, not caring that her voice came and went in the most peculiar way. 'What are you doing here? Why——?'

'You asked me a question,' Mark put in quietly, stopping her dead.

'I did?' she said blankly, hunting back through the time since he had appeared beside her, wondering just what question he meant.

Mark inclined his head slightly, half lifted the hand she had so recently and reluctantly relinquished as if he would take hold of her again, then hesitated and converted the gesture into one of surprising unease, raking it roughly through his thick tawny hair, disturbing its rich smoothness. Seeing how one soft lock fell forward over his forehead, Susannah longed to reach up and ease it back, but hurriedly clamped down hard on the foolish impulse.

'On Good Friday—after the procession—you asked me if I'd ever loved anyone.'

And she had cursed herself for her stupidity ever since. If she had just kept quiet, not pushed things, perhaps... Susannah forced her mind away from its foolish fantasising.

'Oh, that question,' she murmured inanely, not knowing how to respond as she struggled to school her face into an expression that she hoped was totally unrevealing.

It was so hard to say anything because her uncontrollable thoughts wouldn't concentrate on her words; instead they were fixed on the unbelievable fact that Mark was here, in her flat, with her, when she had resigned herself to never seeing him again.

Being with him here, like this, in her familiar surroundings, she found herself more physically aware of him than ever before. He seemed to have grown bigger, stronger, more imposing, though really she knew that that wasn't true and it was only that he seemed so in contrast to the smallness of her room, the soft delicacy of the pale peach and cream décor.

'I couldn't answer you properly then—but I've thought about it a lot since.'

He wasn't making sense, Susannah thought hazily— or perhaps it was that she wasn't listening properly. Dragging her thoughts back from their contemplation of the strength of his jaw, the beautiful shape of his mouth, the painful recollection of how it had felt to have those sensual lips on hers, she tried to concentrate on what he was saying.

'I told you that I didn't know what love was; I'd have been more honest to say that I thought I knew, but I was no longer sure. Now I do know...'

'You do?'

Susannah spoke simply to fill the pause, not really knowing what she was saying. She was afraid to consider the possible repercussions of what he was saying. Had he met some other woman in the past six weeks, someone who had taught him what love meant? She couldn't bear to consider the possibility.

Mark nodded again. 'Love is when you can't live without someone—when everything seems dull and empty because they're not there—when you think of

them the moment you wake and they're there in your
thoughts as you fall asleep—they fill your dreams...'

Now Susannah was nodding along with every phrase,
unable to stop herself. She knew—God, she knew! Mark
was describing exactly how she felt every day.

'But true love is more than that—and that's what I
had to learn. True love isn't selfish or possessive—it
values the other person's feelings more than your own.
When you told me about Simon, I was furious, I hated
the way he had behaved—the selfish, obsessive sort of
love that had trapped you—blackmailed you emotionally
when you couldn't love him back. If you really love
someone you want what's best for them—even if that
means letting them go, leaving them free to be with
someone else...'

Susannah listened, stunned, to what he was saying.
How did he know all this? How could he describe her
situation so perfectly? Dear God, had he guessed——?

'Simon couldn't do that, and I hated him for it—but
then I realised that that was what I had been doing too.'

'*You* ...?'

It was just a weak whisper, all the strength seeming
to have drained out of her in the moment that she had
realised that Mark had stopped speaking in abstract terms
and had used the word 'you'—and the more important
'*I*'.

'I was trying to force you into something I wanted,
and you didn't...'

That wry, shamefaced grin surfaced again, its boyish
appeal tugging at Susannah's heart, but she couldn't
speak, could only wait, in bewildered silence, for him
to go on, afraid even to allow herself to begin to hope
that Mark meant what she was starting to suspect he
might.

'I was trying to hold you, keep you prisoner, because
I couldn't bear to be without you, but you obviously
wanted to be free. I even resorted to blackmail—to my
shame. I know I should never have let you think that
I'd make Andi and Theo pay if you didn't do as I wanted
but I was desperate. I was afraid you'd run out again—
then you gave me a way to make you stay and I couldn't
stop myself from using it.'

Susannah couldn't believe what she was hearing. Had Mark actually used the words 'desperate' and 'afraid'?

'The night of the procession I realised that that made me no better than Simon—that if I really loved you I'd let you go. And so I *tried*, but...'

Mark's hands came up before him, fingers widely spread in a gesture of resigned acceptance.

'I *have* to ask, Susannah—will you marry me? I love you; I want to live with you—my life's empty without you. But if it's not what you want...'

Susannah's head was spinning; she could hardly take this in. Had Mark really said what she thought he had, or was she asleep and dreaming all this?

'If you say no, I won't be like Simon. If you tell me to go, then I will—I'll get out of your life and leave you in peace——'

'No!'

It was all she could manage; her tongue seemed to have turned to wood in her mouth and she shook her head desperately, unable to speak.

The look of despair on Mark's face, draining all colour from it, was like a blow to her heart, bruising it savagely as she saw the light of hope fade from his eyes, leaving them bleak and empty. Still frozen into speechlessness, she watched in disbelief as, without another word, he turned and headed for the door. He actually had it open before she realised what had happened.

'*No!*' Desperation gave her back her voice at last. 'No, Mark—I didn't mean it that way!'

Dashing to his side, she caught hold of his arm, pulling him round to face her. Seeing the confusion in his eyes, the shadowed pain, she knew that he had really meant everything he had said. If she didn't want him, he would not pressurise her as Simon had done. If she hadn't stopped him, he would actually have gone, set her free— he loved her enough for that!

'No, Mark—I didn't mean what you think! I meant to say no—don't go!'

When he appeared unconvinced, his face set in a hard, unrevealing mask, her confidence wavered, weakening her control, and she shook him almost roughly, trying to get through to him.

'*Don't go*, Mark,' she repeated, her voice cracking on the words. 'Please don't leave—you'll break my heart if you do. I need you to stay—I want you—I *love* you!'

It was as if, like some character in a fairy-story, finding her true love turned to stone, she had spoken the magic words needed to break the spell. The ice in Mark's eyes melted swiftly, his whole body suddenly relaxing, his whole face taking on a glow as if lit by a fire from within.

'Say that again,' he commanded huskily, his voice raw and uneven.

'That I love you? Oh, Mark, I do...'

'But——' Mark shook his head dazedly '—I thought that all you wanted was a no-commitment affair—a holiday fling...'

'I thought that was what *you* wanted. Oh, at the beginning, when I wasn't thinking straight, I believed that I wanted something like that because it was so different from the way things had been with Simon—but I couldn't see that it was already a million light-years away from how that had been. I fell head over heels for you, but because I'd always believed that love grew slowly and gradually I didn't recognise what was happening to me. I'll be honest—it scared the hell out of me!'

'Me too,' Mark admitted with a shaken laugh, 'I'd never felt like that before and it knocked me for six. I didn't know how to handle it.'

With a hand that wasn't completely steady, he reached out and cupped the side of Susannah's cheek, giving a faint groan of delight when she turned her lips into his palm and pressed a kiss against it.

'I'd always thought of myself as someone with a fair amount of self-control, but with you it all just evaporated—vanished. I couldn't keep my hands off you, and every time we made love I wanted more...'

Once more he shook his tawny head as if in amazement at himself.

'I knew I should pause—try and get my thoughts into some sort of order—consider where I—we—were going. I felt that the sexual thing—wonderful as it was—just wasn't enough. I wanted something more emotional too—but...'

His eyes darkened, burning down into Susannah's in a way that made her heart leap in excitement.

'Oh, God, Calypso—you were the most gorgeous creature I had ever seen. I felt exactly as Ulysses must have done when he first saw his enchantress and fell under her spell. I was bewitched by you. I would willingly have given up seven years of my life—more—just to be with you. I wanted to talk about how I felt but—there never seemed to be the opportunity.'

His grin was wide, rueful, touched with memories that made Susannah's face flame hotly, recalling them too.

'We didn't exactly do much talking, did we?' she laughed, and Mark shook his head.

'But I thought we'd get round to it eventually. I thought we had plenty of time, and that after a while the passion would—calm down—become a little less overwhelming. I thought it was bound to burn itself out. It couldn't last at that heat.'

Susannah drew in her breath sharply, his words triggering a memory in her mind.

'So—that last night—when you said it couldn't last—that you didn't want it to——'

'You heard that?' Mark broke in sharply. 'You weren't asleep?'

'I thought you meant that you didn't want our relationship to last.'

Mark's head went back in shock, his eyes darkening.

'Dear God, sweetheart—no! I was trying to get myself together—adjust to what had happened. When I said that I didn't want things to go on, I meant in that crazy, unthinking way. I wanted it to cool down—just a little—enough for us to be able to talk calmly about the possibility of a future together.'

'You said it was an act——'

'It was. I couldn't go on pretending it was only a light-hearted, casual affair. I knew I'd have to tell you soon.'

'*Oh*!' Susannah's eyes were dark with distress as she recalled her own interpretation of the things he had said, a very different, and much more damaging one.

'That was one of the reasons why I went out with Theo the next day. I wanted both of us to have time to draw breath—to think. We hadn't been out of each other's company since the moment we met. I knew it was crazy, but I wanted to ask you to marry me then and there—but you said you didn't want commitment so I had to play it your way, even though it nearly killed me to keep up the act. I knew I couldn't keep it to myself any longer, that I'd have to say *something*—but when I got back to the hotel you'd already gone.'

His eyes darkened with a reflection of the pain that had shadowed them then, causing Susannah to bite her lip in distress.

'And you found that appalling note that I'd written,' she said, her voice low and unhappy. 'Mark—about that...'

'You were in a state of shock,' Mark said softly, taking both her hands in his. 'You'd just had the phone call about Simon——'

'No—there was more to it than that. I was angry. You see, you—you said that you weren't looking for any sort of relationship, that it was the last thing on your mind, but that day—in your desk...'

Hot colour flared in her cheeks as she stumbled over her words.

'I—found...'

'You found——? Oh, I see!'

Understanding dawned on Mark's face, driving away his puzzled frown, his eyes lighting with gentle humour.

'Theo,' he said simply.

'Theo?' Susannah echoed, confused.

'I was totally unprepared—mentally and physically—for the impact you had on me—but I knew I had to take responsibility for making sure you were protected—so I turned to Theo. He and Andi had just decided to try for a baby so—I benefited.'

The wry grin was back, this time with a wicked gleam in those golden eyes.

'He was rather over-generous. You must have thought I was planning on at least three full-blown orgies.'

The warm colour which had faded from Susannah's cheeks now came back in full force. 'Something like that,' she admitted, her face a picture of embarrassment. 'So Theo knew?'

'Only that I'd met someone—I didn't mention names. I wasn't ready to make what we had public knowledge—not until I knew exactly where we were going. And I was pretty sure that that was how you wanted things too.'

Susannah nodded slowly. 'I didn't tell Andi until much later. I always wondered why she didn't suspect anything before that, but of course I didn't know then that she and Theo had other things on their minds.'

'It's a pity.' Mark's tone was sombre. 'Perhaps if they had known, then Andi at least might have told me about Simon and I would have been more understanding, realised just what you were going through. As it was, I thought you'd just played me along and then run out on me—but even though I told myself to forget you, I couldn't get you out of my mind—and then, when Theo mentioned that you'd promised to visit, I knew I just had to see you one more time.'

'And I nearly ruined everything by the way I behaved. I'm surprised you didn't hate me.'

'I came close to it,' Mark admitted. 'I was furious—and hurt—a rather deadly combination that did nothing for my ability to think straight. But as soon as I saw you again I knew that everything I had felt for you before hadn't died in the past twelve months. It was still there, and I was determined to keep you with me, no matter what I had to do to achieve it. I even resorted to blackmail, though I knew I could never go through with it. I'm afraid I went about it all wrong—and when I learned the truth about Simon I detested myself for the way I'd behaved.'

'You did have plenty of provocation,' Susannah said gently, unable to let him shoulder all the blame. 'I was as mixed up as you were.'

'Mixed up is right,' Mark laughed. 'I realised I'd been as bad as Simon, and that made me question everything I'd believed about love. I thought I loved you but I bullied you, tried to force you into things against your will, so I had to doubt whether what I'd felt actually *was* love—I no longer even knew what it was.'

'And I went through exactly the same,' Susannah put in softly. 'With Simon, I thought I knew what love was, but then I found how wrong I was. I was so confused that I didn't recognise real love when it hit me in the face—I just thought what I felt for you was nothing but physical passion. And then Simon had that accident, as a result of which I felt so guilty and upset that it distorted my way of looking at things. We've both been a little crazy...'

'Love makes you like that,' Mark said quietly, his fingers tightening on her hands to emphasise the feeling in his words. 'But it also gives you the strength to keep going, to sort things out...'

With infinite gentleness he drew her towards him, his arms moving to enclose her, and Susannah instinctively lifted her face for his kiss.

'We've learned a lot,' she murmured against his cheek.

'Do you think we've learned enough to build a future on?' Mark whispered, punctuating his words with kisses so sweet and gentle that their tenderness tore at her heart.

'I'm sure we have,' she answered, her voice soft and dreamy as she succumbed to the sensual spell he was weaving. 'We both had to learn what love was not, before we could see what it *is*. But now that we understand, then, unlike Calypso and Ulysses, our story can have a happy ending.'

'Oh, no, my love,' Mark corrected gently, his hands beginning to move over her body, to awaken the glowing need that only he could arouse in her. 'This is most definitely not an ending—it's a very happy beginning.'

T

Look out for Temptation's bright, new, stylish covers...

They're Terrifically Tempting!

We're sure you'll love the new raspberry-coloured Temptation books—our brand new look from December.

Temptation romances are still as passionate and fun-loving as ever and they're on sale now!

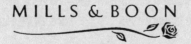

Cruel Legacy

One man's untimely death deprives a wife of her husband, robs a man of his job and offers someone else the chance of a lifetime...

Suicide — the only way out for Andrew Ryecart, facing crippling debt. An end to his troubles, but for those he leaves behind the problems are just beginning, as the repercussions of this most desperate of acts reach out and touch the lives of six different people — changing them forever.

Special large-format paperback edition

OCTOBER
£8.99

W❂RLDWIDE

Next Month's Romances

Each month you can choose from a wide variety of romance with Mills & Boon. Below are the new titles to look out for next month, why not ask either Mills & Boon Reader Service or your Newsagent to reserve you a copy of the titles you want to buy – just tick the titles you would like and either post to Reader Service or take it to any Newsagent and ask them to order your books.

Please save me the following titles:	Please tick	✓
TRIAL BY MARRIAGE	*Lindsay Armstrong*	
ONE FATEFUL SUMMER	*Margaret Way*	
WAR OF LOVE	*Carole Mortimer*	
A SECRET INFATUATION	*Betty Neels*	
ANGELS DO HAVE WINGS	*Helen Brooks*	
MOONSHADOW MAN	*Jessica Hart*	
SWEET DESIRE	*Rosemary Badger*	
NO TIES	*Rosemary Gibson*	
A PHYSICAL AFFAIR	*Lynsey Stevens*	
TRIAL IN THE SUN	*Kay Thorpe*	
IT STARTED WITH A KISS	*Mary Lyons*	
A BURNING PASSION	*Cathy Williams*	
GAMES LOVERS PLAY	*Rosemary Carter*	
HOT NOVEMBER	*Ann Charlton*	
DANGEROUS DISCOVERY	*Laura Martin*	
THE UNEXPECTED LANDLORD	*Leigh Michaels*	

If you would like to order these books in addition to your regular subscription from Mills & Boon Reader Service please send £1.90 per title to: Mills & Boon Reader Service, Freepost, P.O. Box 236, Croydon, Surrey, CR9 9EL, quote your Subscriber No:................................. (if applicable) and complete the name and address details below. Alternatively, these books are available from many local Newsagents including W H Smith, J Menzies, Martins and other paperback stockists from 13 January 1995.

Name:..

Address:..

................................Post Code:........................

To Retailer: If you would like to stock M&B books please contact your regular book/magazine wholesaler for details.